Working Words in Spelling

G. Willard Woodruff and George N. Moore
with Robert G. Forest, Richard A. Talbot, Ann R. Talbot

 D.C. Heath and Company
Lexington, Massachusetts / Toronto, Ontario

HEATH

CONTENTS

Acknowledgments follow on page 176.

International Standard Book Number: 0-669-20683-0

2 3 4 5 6 7 8 9 0

Become a **S-H-A-R-P** Speller

See the word.

- Look at the word.
- Think about the letters that spell the word.

Hear the word.

- Say the word.
- Listen to the consonant and vowel sounds.

Adopt the word.

- Close your eyes.
- See the word in your mind's eye.
- Think how it looks and sounds.

Record the word.

- Cover the word.
- Write the word.

Proofread the word.

- Correct the word.
- Touch each letter.
- Think about the word again.

1

A. Pretest Write each spelling word.

B. Spelling Words and Phrases

1.	spade	will <u>spade</u> the garden
2.	salesperson	<u>salesperson</u> at the door
3.	pavement	cracks in the <u>pavement</u>
4.	behave	should <u>behave</u> better
5.	locate	will try to <u>locate</u> it
6.	grateful	<u>grateful</u> for the favor
7.	debate	an angry <u>debate</u>
8.	rating	were <u>rating</u> their work
9.	estate	a huge private <u>estate</u>
10.	haste	too much <u>haste</u>
11.	bathe	will <u>bathe</u> with warm water
12.	ache	a constant <u>ache</u>
13.	headache	cured my <u>headache</u>
14.	calendar	a school <u>calendar</u>
15.	vanish	to <u>vanish</u> without a sign
16.	sandwich	peanut butter <u>sandwich</u>
17.	anxious	was very <u>anxious</u>
18.	champion	want to be <u>champion</u>
19.	establish	to <u>establish</u> a colony
20.	disaster	to avoid <u>disaster</u>

Other Word Forms

spaded, spading	bathes, bathed, bathing
salespeople	ached, aching
pave, paving	headaches
behaves, behaving, behavior	calendars
locates, locating, location	vanishes, vanished, vanishing
gratefully	sandwiches, sandwiched
debated, debating, debater	anxiously
rate, rated, ratings	championship
estates	establishes, established, establishment
hastily	disastrous

C. Visual Warm-up Write each word in its correct shape.

a.

b.

c.

d.

e.

f.

g.

h.

i.

j.

k.

l.

m.

n.

o.

p.

q.

r.

s.

t.

D. Break the Code Use the code to write the spelling words.

a	b	c	d	e	f	g	h	i	j	k	l	m	n	o	p	q	r	s	t	u	v	w	x	y	z
↓	↓	↓	↓	↓	↓	↓	↓	↓	↓	↓	↓	↓	↓	↓	↓	↓	↓	↓	↓	↓	↓	↓	↓	↓	↓
p	e	g	s	v	k	x	m	c	f	h	t	i	u	r	b	a	o	q	d	z	n	l	y	w	j

1. qikb   ~~st~~ ache
2. eqvmdk   ~~ea~~ vanish
3. pbkqeb   behave
4. daqtb   spade
5. bdlqpwmdk   _____
6. coqlbjnw   _____
7. oqlmvc   _____
8. qvgmrnd   _____
9. kqdlb   haste
10. dqwbdabodrv   salesperson
11. wriqlb   locate
12. tmdqdlbo   disaster
13. kbqtqikb   headache
14. dqvtymik   sandwich
15. tbpqlb   debate
16. aqebhbvl   pavement
17. iqwbvtqo   calendar
18. bdlqlb   estate
19. ikqhamrv   champion
20. pqlkb   bathe

E. Generally Speaking Write each spelling word for the group it best fits.

1. head pain, discomfort, ᴀ head ache
2. shovel, digging tool, spade
3. appreciative, thankful, grateful
4. sidewalk, concrete, pavement
5. set up, arrange, establish
6. date, appointment book, calender
7. winner, the best, champion
8. disappear, go from sight, vanish
9. grading, judging, rating
10. property, mansion, estate
11. tragedy, misfortune, disaster
12. quickness, hurry, haste
13. control oneself, act, behave
14. argue, dispute, debate
15. shower, wash, bathe
16. worried, concerned, anxious
17. lunch, bread, sandwich
18. seller, clerk, salesperson
19. find, place, locate
20. pain, hurt, ache

Spelling Words

	spade	salesperson	pavement	behave	locate
	grateful	debate	rating	estate	haste
	bathe	ache	headache	calendar	vanish
	sandwich	anxious	champion	establish	disaster

F. Context Clues Solve the word mysteries by using spelling words. Write the words.

1. The water is ready. I will _____ the baby.

2. I have been lifting weights. My arms _____ .

3. The magician pulled a scarf out of my ear. Then he seemed to make the scarf _____ into thin air.

4. The students chose a science problem for discussion. They will _____ it next week.

5. My friend is a gold medal winner. She is a _____ .

6. The damage caused by the flood was terrible. It was a _____ .

7. The clerk will assist you with your purchase. He is a _____ .

8. Do not hurry. Work done in _____ makes waste.

9. Upon her death, her property was claimed by many. The court settled the _____ .

10. My dog was missing last week. I was worried and _____ until I found her.

11. I have to lie down. I have a splitting _____ .

12. The car was stolen two days ago. We have not been able to _____ it yet.

13. We had to dig up the yard to start a garden. We used a _____ .

14. I think my birthday is on a Thursday. Please check the _____ .

15. You cannot vote in that district. You must first _____ residence.

16. Children, please do not throw your crayons! You must _____ .

17. That stock is a good investment. It has a high _____ .

G. Using Other Word Forms Write the Other Word Form (p. 4) that completes each sentence.

1. He was not acting properly. He was _____ (behave) poorly.

2. My house is close to everything. It's in a handy _____ (locate).

3. Her foot throbbed with pain. It was _____ (ache).

4. She worked too quickly. She finished too _____ (haste).

5. Everything went wrong. The whole project was _____ (disaster).

H. Challenge Words Write the Challenge Word that fits each group of words.

capsule	dramatically	gravity	fragrance	frantic

1. anxious, raving, panicky, _____

2. space, flight, container, _____

3. actor, speaks, vividly _____

4. plant, flower, scent, _____

5. goes up, comes down, force, _____

I. Spelling and Writing Write in your journal. Use as many of the Spelling Words, Other Word Forms, and Challenge Words as you can to write a page about a big storm you have seen. Then circle the spelling words you used. Remember when writing a journal to include the date, the time, and what happened. Proofread your spelling.

Example: *April 23–5:00—Today during the big storm, the rough* (pavement) *seemed to* (vanish) *under a smooth surface of water.*

2

A. Pretest Write each spelling word.

B. Spelling Words and Phrases

1. evil — an evil deed
2. equal — must be equal
3. decent — decent behavior
4. recent — a recent event
5. meter — had read the water meter
6. medium — small, medium, or large
7. senior — a senior in high school
8. scene — scene of the crime
9. complete — when I complete it
10. supreme — a supreme effort
11. serious — a serious problem
12. severe — that severe blizzard
13. cheap — at a cheap price
14. treaty — signed the treaty
15. lease — a yearly lease
16. eager — an eager beginning
17. uneasy — an uneasy feeling
18. gear — shifted into low gear
19. disappear — might suddenly disappear
20. reflection — saw my reflection

Other Word Forms

evilly, evilness
equaled, equaling,
  equally, equality
decently, decency,
recently
metered, metric
media, median
seniority
scenery
completed, completing,
  completely, completion
supremely
seriously, seriousness
severely, severity
cheaper, cheaply
treaties
leases, leasing
eagerly, eagerness
easy, uneasily
gears, geared
appear, disappeared,
  disappearance
reflect, reflected,
  reflecting, reflections

C. Visual Warm-up Write each word in its correct shape.

a.
b.
c.
d.
e.
f.
g.
h.
i.
j.
k.
l.
m.
n.
o.
p.
q.
r.
s.
t.

D. Sort Your Vowels Write each spelling word in the correct list. A word may be used more than once.

Long *e* Sound Spelled *e*

1. _____
2. _____
3. _____
4. _____
5. _____
6. _____
7. _____
8. _____
9. _____
10. _____

Long *e* Sound Spelled *ea*

11. _____
12. _____
13. _____
14. _____
15. _____

e* and *ea* Controlled by *r

16. _____
17. _____
18. _____
19. _____
20. _____
21. _____

***tion* Ending**

22. _____

E. Change a Word Rearrange the letters in each underlined word to find a word from the spelling list. Write the word.

1. We visited the <u>center</u> of government on a _____ field trip.

2. Does that _____ creature <u>live</u> in this cave?

3. In a <u>rage</u>, the campers gathered their _____ and drove off.

4. I bought the <u>peach</u> for a _____ price.

5. The artist was forced to _____ an <u>easel</u>.

6. Both nations were _____ to <u>agree</u> to a truce.

Spelling Words

evil	*equal*	*decent*	*recent*	*meter*
medium	*senior*	*scene*	*complete*	*supreme*
serious	*severe*	*cheap*	*treaty*	*lease*
eager	*uneasy*	*gear*	*disappear*	*reflection*

F. Crossword Puzzle Solve the puzzle by using all the words from the spelling list. Write the words. Check your answers in the **Spelling Dictionary**.

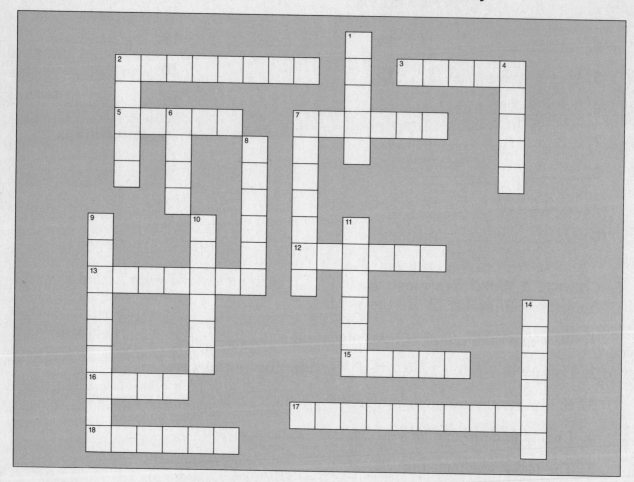

Across

2. to finish

3. the same

5. anxious to do something

7. elder

12. nervous; restless

13. highest; greatest

15. a unit of measure

16. wicked

17. a likeness or image

18. not long ago

Down

1. a view

2. inexpensive

4. to rent

6. equipment

7. thoughtful; grave

8. harsh

9. to vanish

10. a written agreement between nations

11. between small and large

14. good; proper

G. Using Other Word Forms Write the Other Word Form (p. 8) that completes each sentence.

1. The wicked thief smiled _____ (evil) as she took the money.

2. He was ill because he was _____ (severe) sunburned.

3. She moved _____ (uneasy) as she entered the darkened room.

4. Common _____ (decent) is a worthy characteristic.

5. The President signed several _____ (treaty) with his enemies.

H. Challenge Words Write the Challenge Word that completes each sentence.

adhesive	allegiance	appealing	keyboard	extremely

1. If an idea interests you, it may be very _____ .

2. If she has a lot of work to do, she is _____ busy.

3. If you are using a new kind of glue, you're using a new _____ .

4. If you enter data into the computer, you use a _____ .

5. If you salute the flag, you pledge your _____ .

I. Spelling and Writing Use as many of the Spelling Words, Other Word Forms, and Challenge Words as you can in sentences about a science-fiction adventure you have imagined. Then circle the spelling words you used. Proofread your spelling.

Example: *We were* (*eager*) *to* (*complete*) *the mission beneath the sea.*

3

A. Pretest Write each spelling word.

B. Spelling Words and Phrases

1.	vice	no bad habit or _vice_
2.	tile	a loose _tile_ in the floor
3.	spite	in _spite_ of the weather
4.	mining	_mining_ for gold
5.	idle	don't like to be _idle_
6.	diet	now on a _diet_
7.	diamond	sparkled like a _diamond_
8.	finally	_finally_ packed
9.	trial	giving it a _trial_
10.	quietly	to talk _quietly_
11.	reliable	a _reliable_ friend
12.	infant	fed the _infant_
13.	instant	started at the same _instant_
14.	distant	the _distant_ mountain
15.	linen	made with _linen_
16.	sicken	to _sicken_ with fear
17.	nickel	not much for a _nickel_
18.	pickle	a very crisp _pickle_
19.	tickled	_tickled_ my nose
20.	sprinkle	a light _sprinkle_ of rain

Other Word Forms

vices, vicious
tiles, tiled, tiling
spited, spiting, spiteful
mine, miner
idled, idling, idly
dieted, dieting, dieter
diamonds
final, finals
trials
quiet
rely
infants, infancy

instantly
distantly, distance
linens
sick, sickens,
  sickening, sickly
nickels
pickles, pickled,
  pickling
tickle, tickling,
  ticklish
sprinkles, sprinkled,
  sprinkling

C. Visual Warm-up Write each word in its correct shape.

a.
b.
c.
d.
e.
f.
g.
h.
i.
j.
k.
l.
m.
n.
o.
p.
q.
r.
s.
t.

D. Rhyming Words

Write the words from the spelling list that rhyme with each of the words.

1. chicken _____

2. dining _____

3. quiet _____

4. dial _____

_____

5. undeniable _____

6. spice _____

7. sickle _____

_____

8. crinkle _____

9. quite _____

10. bridal _____

11. trickled _____

12. Write the three words not used above that rhyme with each other.

a. _____ **b.** _____ **c.** _____

13. Write the four words that did not rhyme with any of the words above.

a. _____ **c.** _____

b. _____ **d.** _____

E. Missing Vowels Find the missing vowels and write the spelling words.

1. m __ n __ ng _____

2. __ nf __ nt _____

3. l __ n __ n _____

4. p __ ckl __ _____

5. spr __ nkl __ _____

6. f __ n __ lly _____

7. d __ __ m __ nd _____

8. q __ __ __ tly _____

9. d __ st __ nt _____

10. t __ ckl __ d _____

11. r __ l __ __ bl __ _____

12. s __ ck __ n _____

F. Be a Word Detective Remove one letter from each word in parentheses to find a word from the spelling list. Write the word.

1. The audience loved them in _____ (sprite) of their poor performance.

2. A bad habit can be a _____ (voice).

3. The feather _____ (trickled) my nose.

4. A _____ (prickle) is made from a cucumber.

Spelling Words

vice	tile	spite	mining	idle	diet
diamond	finally	trial	quietly	reliable	infant
instant	distant	linen	sicken	nickel	pickle
tickled	sprinkle				

G. Finding Words The words in the spelling list appear in the beginning (A-H), middle (I-Q), or end (R-Z) of the **Spelling Dictionary**. Write each word.

Beginning
A-H

1. _____
2. _____
3. _____
4. _____

Middle
I-Q

5. _____
6. _____
7. _____
8. _____
9. _____
10. _____
11. _____
12. _____

End
R-Z

13. _____
14. _____
15. _____
16. _____
17. _____
18. _____
19. _____
20. _____

H. Generally Speaking Write a spelling word for the group it best fits.

1. steady, dependable, _____

2. penny, dime, _____

3. shower, water, _____

4. baby, child, _____

5. far, not close, _____

6. moment, second, _____

7. precious stone, gem, _____

8. silently, softly, _____

9. at last, at an end, _____

10. upset, make ill, _____

11. thin square, plastic piece, _____

I. Using Other Word Forms Add an ending to each word to write an Other Word Form (p. 12).

1. tickle + ish = _____

2. spite + ing = _____

3. idle + ing = _____

4. sprinkle + ed = _____

5. infant + cy = _____

6. What letter gets subtracted in the first four words? _____

J. Challenge Words Write the Challenge Word that completes each analogy.

distrust	drifting	prism	resign	violence

1. color is to **red** as **shape** is to _____

2. land is to **wandering** as **sea** is to _____

3. faith is to **confidence** as **doubt** is to _____

4. enter is to **enlist** as **leave** is to _____

5. calm is to **serenity** as **fury** is to _____

K. Spelling and Writing Write each set of words in a sentence. You may use Other Word Forms. Proofread your spelling.

Example: infant – finally – quietly *The cats sang quietly after the infant finally stopped crying.*

1. vice – spite – idle

2. mining – distant – diamond

3. sicken – diet – pickle

4. tile – sprinkle – instant

5. reliable – trial – nickel

6. linen – tickled

4

A. Pretest Write each spelling word.

B. Spelling Words and Phrases

1.	sole	on the sole of my shoe
2.	throne	was placed on the throne
3.	postage	forgot the postage stamp
4.	postpone	can't postpone the meeting
5.	cooperate	asked them to cooperate
6.	ghost	never saw a ghost
7.	stroll	liked to stroll together
8.	thrown	will be thrown out
9.	organize	to organize a second team
10.	force	the force of the water
11.	perform	loves to perform
12.	reform	must reform behavior
13.	resort	a summer resort
14.	import	went to the import store
15.	explore	want to explore the cave
16.	enforce	a way to enforce the law
17.	according	according to our records
18.	broad	a broad avenue
19.	abroad	a trip abroad to Greece
20.	coarse	coarse texture of cloth

Other Word Forms

soles, soled
thrones
post, postal
postponed, postponing,
    postponement
cooperated, cooperation
ghostly
strolled,
    stroller
throw, threw
organized, organization,
    organizer
forced, forcibly

performed, performer,
    performance
reformed, reformer
resorts, resorted
imports, importer
explores, explored,
    exploring, explorer,
    exploration
enforced, enforcer
accord
broader, broadly
coarser, coarsest,
    coarsely

C. Visual Warm-up Write each word in its correct shape.

a.

b.

c.

d.

e.

f.

g.

h.

i.

j.

k.

l.

m.

n.

o.

p.

q.

r.

s.

t.

D. Scrambled Words Unscramble the scrambled word to find the spelling word that completes the sentence. Write the word.

1. The actors will _____ (rmofrep) every evening for two weeks.

2. I enjoy a leisurely _____ (lolstr) through the park.

3. How much _____ (stopeag) did the letter require?

4. We _____ (oprtim) cheese from other countries.

5. _____ (ngrdaiocc) to my records, the bill was never paid.

6. Adventurers _____ (pleexor) faraway lands.

7. If we _____ (rooteeapc), we will succeed in solving the problem.

8. The vacation _____ (rtsero) is in Florida.

9. The clown always wears a _____ (daobr) smile.

10. The _____ (coref) of the river carried me into deep water.

11. We sailed _____ (adaobr) on the ocean liner.

12. Blackbeard's _____ (stogh) still haunts the island.

13. The mayoral candidate is calling for a tax _____ (fororm).

14. We must _____ (stoneopp) the meeting until Saturday.

15. The new secretary was hired to _____ (neogairz) the files.

E. Finding Words The words in the spelling list appear in the beginning (A-H), middle (I-Q), or end (R-Z) of the **Spelling Dictionary**. Write each word.

Beginning A-H	Middle I-Q	End R-Z
1. _____	10. _____	15. _____
2. _____	11. _____	16. _____
3. _____	12. _____	17. _____
4. _____	13. _____	18. _____
5. _____	14. _____	19. _____
6. _____		20. _____
7. _____		
8. _____		
9. _____		

Spelling Words

sole	*throne*	*postage*	*postpone*	*cooperate*
ghost	*stroll*	*thrown*	*organize*	*force*
perform	*reform*	*resort*	*import*	*explore*
enforce	*according*	*broad*	*abroad*	*coarse*

F. Word Search The spelling words and some Other Word Forms (p. 16) can be found in the grid below. The words appear across and down. Circle and write the words.

Spelling Words

Across

```
r e f o r m i s n i r o a e
e f o r c e d o e e e d b x
s t h r o w n l g n x s r p
o r g a n i z e b f p c o l
r p f c s o l e s o l o a o
t h r o n e e o b r o a d r
t t s o g h o s t c r r p i
i s l p c o a r s e e s e n
m w a e s t r o l l l e r g
p f o r c e i w t i l r f t
o a l a p o s t p o n e o h
r n l t s t r o l l e d r r
t e r e i p o s t a g e m e
d a c c o r d i n g j p i w
```

1. _____

2. _____

3. _____

4. _____

5. _____

6. _____

7. _____

8. _____

9. _____

10. _____

11. _____

12. _____

Other Word Forms

Across

21. _____

22. _____

23. _____

Down

24. _____

25. _____

26. _____

Down

13. _____

14. _____

15. _____

16. _____

17. _____

18. _____

19. _____

20. _____

G. Using Other Word Forms Write the Other Word Form (p. 16) that fits each clue.

1. widely _____ (broad)

2. putting off _____ (postpone)

3. searching around _____ (explore)

4. rougher _____ (coarse)

5. teamwork _____ (cooperate)

H. Challenge Words Write the Challenge Word that completes each sentence.

forgery	doughnut	fortress	moral	notify

1. Every fable ends with a _____ .

2. Please _____ us about any change of plans.

3. The child's toy is shaped like a _____ .

4. A castle is an old-time _____ .

5. To sign another person's name to a legal document is _____ .

I. Spelling and Writing Write each set of words in a sentence. You may use Other Word Forms. Proofread your spelling.

Example: postpone – perform – resort *The band postponed its performance at the resort.*

1. postage – thrown – stroll

2. according – sole – explore

3. ghost – organize – force

4. reform – enforce – broad

5. throne – abroad – import

6. coarse – cooperate

MT. KATAHDIN AMC LODGE

5

A. Pretest Write each spelling word.

B. Spelling Words and Phrases

1. refuse — didn't dare to refuse
2. confuse — doesn't confuse me
3. dispute — a dispute about the goal
4. amusement — into the amusement park
5. useless — because it's useless
6. issue — the new magazine issue
7. statue — stood like a statue
8. value — of little value
9. valuable — a valuable painting
10. discontinue — will discontinue the model
11. union — joined the labor union
12. human — the strongest human alive
13. humor — the book of humor
14. jury — met with the jury
15. curious — a curious cat
16. figure — if you can figure out
17. future — sometime in the future
18. injure — might injure your hand
19. insure — will insure the package
20. capture — will capture the flag

Other Word Forms

refused, refusing, refusal	unionized, unions
confusing, confusion	humanity, humanly
disputed, disputing	humorous, humorist
amuse, amusing, amusements	juries
use, uselessly, uselessness	curiosity, curiousness
issues, issued, issuing	figured, figurine
statues, statuette	futuristic
values, valued, valuing	injuring, injurious
continue, discontinued	insuring, insurance
	captured, capturing

C. Visual Warm-up Write each word in its correct shape.

a.

b.

c.

d.

e.

f.

g.

h.

i.

j.

k.

l.

m.

n.

o.

p.

q.

r.

s.

t.

D. All in a Row Write the twenty spelling words in alphabetical order. Then join the boxed letters and write four hidden words.

1. _ _ _ _ _ _ _ □
2. _ _ _ _ _ □ _ _
3. _ □ _ _ _ _ _
4. _ _ _ _ _ _ □ _
5. _ _ _ _ _ □ _ _ _
6. Hidden Word: _____
7. _ _ _ _ □ _ _
8. _ _ _ _ □ _ _
9. _ _ _ _ □ _
10. _ _ □ _ _
11. _ _ _ □□ _
12. Hidden Word: _____

13. □ _ _ _ _ _
14. _ □ _ _ _ _
15. _ □ _ □ _
16. _ _ □ _
17. _ _ _ _ □
18. Hidden Word: _____
19. _ _ _ □ _ _
20. _ _ □ _ □ _
21. □ _ _ _ _ _
22. _ _ _ _ _ □
23. _ □ _ _ _
24. Hidden Word: _____

E. Fan Out Write the spelling word formed by each combination.

1. _____   fig

2. _____   fut

3. _____   inj   + ure

4. _____   ins

5. _____   capt

Spelling Words

refuse	confuse	dispute	amusement	useless
issue	statue	value	valuable	discontinue
union	human	humor	jury	curious
figure	future	injure	insure	capture

F. Bases, Prefixes, and Suffixes The spelling list contains sixteen base words and four words with prefixes or suffixes. Write each spelling word.

Words with Prefixes or Suffixes   **Base Words**

1. figurine _____

2. confusion _____

3. humorous _____

4. curiosity _____

5. injurious _____

6. refusal _____

7. issues _____

8. insurance _____

9. humanity _____

10. statuette _____

Words with Prefixes or Suffixes   **Base Words**

11. captured _____

12. disputed _____

13. valuing _____

14. futuristic _____

15. unionized _____

16. juries _____

17. _____ use

18. _____ value

19. _____ amuse

20. _____ continue

G. Using Other Word Forms Add an ending to each word to write an Other Word Form (p. 20).

1. dispute + ing = _____

2. amuse + ing = _____

3. issue + ing = _____

4. injure + ing = _____

5. capture + ing = _____

6. What letter gets subtracted each time? _____

H. Challenge Words Write the Challenge Word that fits each group of words.

commute	urged	unique	utensils	youthful

1. pleaded, prodded, _____

2. young, immature, _____

3. tools, silverware, _____

4. unequaled, unusual, _____

5. drive, travel, _____

I. Spelling and Writing Write the following phrases in sentences. Proofread your spelling.

Example: *He has a sense of humor.*

1. sense of <u>humor</u>
2. their <u>amusement</u>
3. <u>useless</u> machine
4. silly <u>dispute</u>
5. on the <u>statue</u>
6. <u>valuable</u> stamp
7. <u>curious</u> children
8. <u>shadowy</u> figure
9. confused the <u>jury</u>
10. <u>future</u> plans

11. will need to <u>insure</u>
12. may <u>injure</u> my back
13. current <u>issue</u>
14. to <u>capture</u> the flag
15. <u>union</u> meeting
16. <u>human</u> nature
17. will <u>discontinue</u> the show
18. to <u>confuse</u> the class
19. may <u>refuse</u> to go
20. of little <u>value</u>

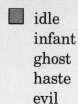

6

R
E
V
I
E
W

■ idle	★ anxious	▲ establish	◆ statue	● salesperson
infant	eager	resort	recent	cheap
ghost	instant	mining	spade	refuse
haste	throne	organize	enforce	complete
evil	diamond	issue	curious	human

A. Word Operations Unscramble each scrambled word to form a spelling word. The shape tells you in what column you can find the spelling word. Write the word. Then perform one or two operations on each word to write Other Word Forms.

		Spelling Words	**Operations**	**Other Word Forms**
1. lide	= ■	_____	+ ness	= _____
2. blishatse	= ▲	_____	+ ment	= _____
3. manhu	= ●	_____	+ ity	= _____
4. ragee	= ★	_____	+ ly	= _____
5. live	= ■	_____	+ s	= _____
6. nagorize	= ▲	_____	− e + ing	= _____
7. chape	= ●	_____	+ ly	= _____
8. daesp	= ◆	_____	+ s	= _____
9. center	= ◆	_____	+ ly	= _____
10. onethr	= ★	_____	+ s	= _____
11. forence	= ◆	_____	+ ment	= _____
12. fuseer	= ●	_____	+ s	= _____
13. hesta	= ■	_____	− e + ens	= _____
14. sorter	= ▲	_____	+ ing	= _____
15. siouxan	= ★	_____	+ ly	= _____
16. ingmin	= ▲	_____	− ing + ers	= _____
17. pleetmoc	= ●	_____	+ ly	= _____
18. rucsiou	= ◆	_____	− us + sity	= _____
19. stogh	= ■	_____	+ ly	= _____
20. stantin	= ★	_____	+ ly	= _____
21. sueis	= ▲	_____	− e + ing	= _____
22. stueta	= ◆	_____	+ s	= _____
23. mondaid	= ★	_____	+ s	= _____
24. fantin	= ■	_____	− t + cy	= _____
25. ponserselas	= ●	_____	make plural	= _____

■ calendar   ★ tile   ▲ debate   ◆ according   ● equal
tickled   dispute   spite   jury   disaster
insure   rating   future   distant   trial
decent   abroad   lease   reform   treaty
medium   broad   grateful   import   union

B. Words in Blanks Choose Other Word Forms or the spelling words that complete the sentences. Write the words. The shape tells you in what column you can find the spelling word. Write each word or its Other Word Form only once. If you need help, use the **Spelling Dictionary**.

1. The kitchen ★ _____ were cut ● _____ on all sides.

2. No one ★ _____ the fact that ■ _____ are helpful.

3. The ★ _____ for the new television show are low,

◆ _____ to the newscaster.

4. Lawyers have always ▲ _____ the ways ◆ _____
are selected.

5. Heavy smoke in the ◆ _____ signaled a ● _____ fire.

6. In ▲ _____ of my collar, the feathers on my hat kept

■ _____ my neck.

7. The lawyers traveled ★ _____ to study court

● _____ in Europe.

8. Saving money may ■ _____ a good ▲ _____ .

9. By ◆ _____ your study habits, you can get ■ _____
marks on your report card.

10. One company ◆ _____ typewriters and ▲ _____
them to offices.

11. Though we are both of ■ _____ height, my shoulders are

★ _____ than yours.

12. Peace ● _____ are often ▲ _____ accepted by
warring nations.

13. There are many labor ● _____ in our country.

■ sandwich   ★ behave   ▲ bathe   ◆ headache   ● ache
senior   disappear   reflection   scene   meter
diet   nickel   sprinkle   pickle   quietly
thrown   stroll   explore   postage   cooperate
injure   amusement   capture   valuable   discontinue

C. Word Clues Write the spelling word that goes with each clue. The shape tells you in what column you can find the spelling word. Then write an Other Word Form for each spelling word.

Word Clues	Spelling Words	Other Word Forms
1. to harm ■		
2. worth a lot of money ◆		
3. a likeness ▲		
4. five cents ★		
5. to work together ●		
6. a special food plan ■		
7. a continuous pain ●		
8. a view ◆		
9. tossed ■		
10. to wash ▲		
11. the cost to mail a letter ◆		
12. anything that entertains ★		
13. to end ●		
14. a light rain ▲		
15. a lunchtime food ■		
16. a pain in the head ◆		
17. to control oneself ★		
18. without much noise ●		
19. search an unfamiliar place ▲		
20. made from a cucumber ◆		
21. to walk for pleasure ★		
22. fourth year of high school ■		
23. a unit of length ●		
24. to take by force ▲		
25. to vanish ★		

gear	locate	pavement	vanish	estate
supreme	figure	serious	confuse	value
sicken	linen	reliable	finally	vice
postpone	perform	force	coarse	sole
uneasy	humor	champion	severe	useless

D. Sentence Completion Choose Other Word Forms or the spelling words to replace the words printed under the blanks. Write the words. If you need help, use the **Spelling Dictionary**.

1. We _____ the play today because it was _____
   <u>perform</u>   <u>postpone</u>
   yesterday.

2. I _____ on the cobbler to mend the _____ of my shoes.
   <u>reliable</u>   <u>sole</u>

3. Our newly _____ driveway has a much _____
   <u>pavement</u>   <u>coarse</u>
   surface than most.

4. Each New Year, some people try _____ to give up their bad habits,
   <u>serious</u>

   or _____ .
   <u>vice</u>

5. We _____ all ten _____ on our bicycles to pedal uphill.
   <u>useless</u>   <u>gear</u>

6. Some people are _____ telling _____ stories.
   <u>uneasy</u>   <u>humor</u>

7. Three private _____ are _____ near the ocean.
   <u>estate</u>   <u>locate</u>

8. Though I felt _____ to my stomach before class, I
   <u>sicken</u>
   _____ myself to redo my math _____ .
   <u>force</u>   <u>figure</u>

9. My _____ stamp collection was damaged _____
   <u>value</u>   <u>severe</u>
   during the flood.

10. When I couldn't find the bed _____ , I was sure they had
    <u>linen</u>

    _____ .
    <u>vanish</u>

11. The tennis match for the _____ was played _____ .
    <u>champion</u>   <u>supreme</u>

12. I became _____ during the _____ exam in math class.
    <u>confuse</u>   <u>finally</u>

7

A. Pretest Write each spelling word.

B. Spelling Words and Phrases

1.	raid	a raid at night
2.	vain	tried in vain
3.	raisin	raisin and nut bread
4.	claims	claims the prize
5.	exclaim	will exclaim angrily
6.	contain	a box to contain supplies
7.	attain	will attain our goals
8.	obtain	will obtain another one
9.	entertain	likes to entertain
10.	explain	no need to explain
11.	chamber	a secret chamber
12.	mass	a swarming mass of hornets
13.	rascal	called me a rascal
14.	staff	met with the staff
15.	standard	a standard size
16.	exact	the exact change
17.	unpack	had to unpack in the dark
18.	margin	the margin on the left
19.	bargain	made a bargain
20.	uncertain	uncertain future

Other Word Forms

raided, raider
vainly, vanity
raisins
claim, claiming
exclaimed, exclamation
containing, container
attains, attained
obtaining, obtainable
entertainer,
  entertainment
explained, explaining,
  explanation
chambers
masses, massed
rascals
staffed, staffing
standards
exactness, exactly
pack, unpacked,
  unpacking
marginal
bargained, bargainer
certain, uncertainty

C. Visual Warm-up Write each word in its correct shape.

a.

b.

c.

d.

e.

f.

g.

h.

i.

j.

k.

l.

m.

n.

o.

p.

q.

r.

s.

t.

D. Synonym Puzzles Find a synonym from the spelling list to complete each puzzle. Write each word. Use the **Spelling Dictionary**.

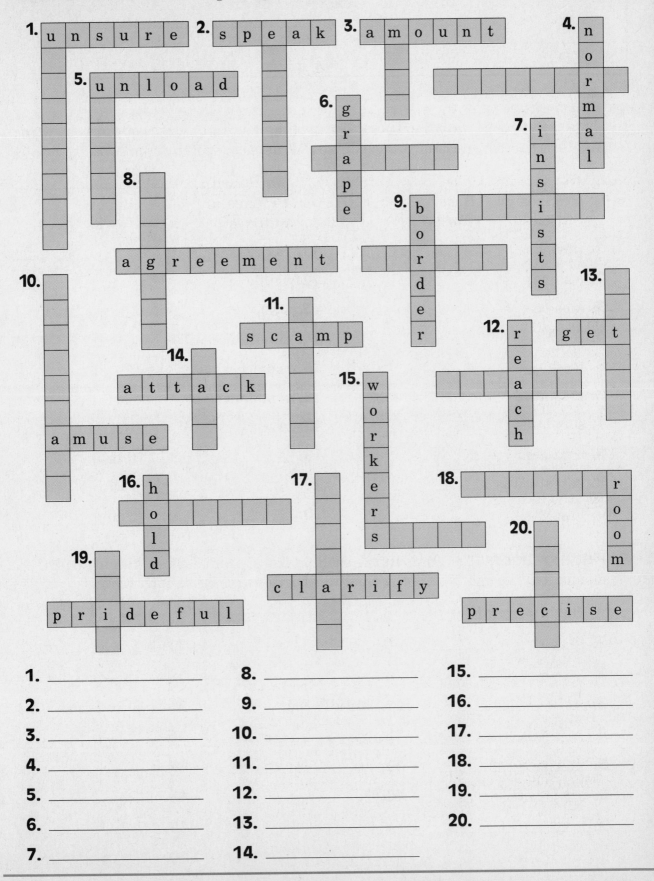

1. _____

2. _____

3. _____

4. _____

5. _____

6. _____

7. _____

8. _____

9. _____

10. _____

11. _____

12. _____

13. _____

14. _____

15. _____

16. _____

17. _____

18. _____

19. _____

20. _____

Spelling Words

raid	vain	raisin	claims	exclaim
contain	attain	obtain	entertain	explain
chamber	mass	rascal	staff	standard
exact	unpack	margin	bargain	uncertain

E. Bases, Prefixes, and Suffixes The spelling list contains seventeen base words and three words with prefixes or suffixes. Write each spelling word.

Words with Prefixes or Suffixes   **Base Words**

1. raisins _____
2. attained _____
3. masses _____
4. container _____
5. rascals _____
6. exclaimed _____
7. standards _____
8. obtaining _____
9. bargained _____
10. marginal _____

Words with Prefixes or Suffixes   **Base Words**

11. raider _____
12. vainly _____
13. staffed _____
14. entertainment _____
15. chambers _____
16. explaining _____
17. exactly _____
18. _____ certain
19. _____ pack
20. _____ claim

F. Finding Words The words in the spelling list appear in the beginning (A-H), middle (I-Q), or end (R-Z) of the **Spelling Dictionary**. Write each word.

Beginning A-H

1. _____
2. _____
3. _____
4. _____
5. _____
6. _____
7. _____

8. _____
9. _____

Middle I-Q

10. _____
11. _____
12. _____

End R-Z

13. _____
14. _____
15. _____
16. _____
17. _____
18. _____
19. _____
20. _____

G. Using Other Word Forms Write the Other Word Form (p. 28) that completes each sentence.

1. He was unsure. He was filled with _____ (uncertain).

2. She told him how to do it. She gave him a good _____ (explain).

3. They were buying souvenirs. They were _____ (obtain) remembrances.

4. She sang for the audience. She was a good _____ (entertain).

5. The director was hiring counselors. He was _____ (staff) the camp.

H. Challenge Words Write the Challenge Word that completes each sentence.

radiator	baffled	decaying	courageous	incapable

1. We'll remove all _____ branches.

2. We can't afford to hire _____ workers.

3. The audience was _____ by the illusion.

4. You need more water in the car _____ .

5. The pioneers were a _____ group of people.

I. Spelling and Writing Write in your journal. Use as many of the Spelling Words, Other Word Forms, and Challenge Words as you can to write a page about a haunted house you might visit on Halloween. Then circle the spelling words you used. Remember when writing a journal to include the date, the time, and what happened. Proofread your spelling.

Example: *October 31–9:00—I* (exclaimed) *as I* (vainly) *tried*
to get out of the (chamber) .

8

A. Pretest Write each spelling word.

B. Spelling Words and Phrases

1. creep — will <u>creep</u> away
2. speech — forgot the <u>speech</u>
3. squeeze — can't <u>squeeze</u> through
4. weekly — <u>weekly</u> newspaper
5. needless — <u>needless</u> to say
6. proceed — would <u>proceed</u> cautiously
7. agreement — signed the <u>agreement</u>
8. peer — to <u>peer</u> into the dark
9. steer — will <u>steer</u> with both hands
10. brief — a very <u>brief</u> stay
11. grief — hid our <u>grief</u>
12. thief — caught the <u>thief</u>
13. niece — a <u>niece</u> and a nephew
14. pier — at the end of the <u>pier</u>
15. neither — <u>neither</u> here nor there
16. received — <u>received</u> in the mail
17. energy — will save <u>energy</u>
18. machinery — modern <u>machinery</u>
19. convince — will <u>convince</u> the jury
20. medicine — rarely needs <u>medicine</u>

Other Word Forms

crept, creeping, creepy
speeches
squeezes, squeezed,
  squeezing
week
need, needlessly
proceeds, proceeded,
  procedure
agree, agreements
peers, peering
steers, steered, steering
briefly, briefer
grieve, grieves,
  grieving
thieves, theft
nieces
piers
receive, receiving
energies, energize
machine
convinces, convinced,
  convincing
medicines, medicinal

C. Visual Warm-up Write each word in its correct shape.

a.

b.

c.

d.

e.

f.

g.

h.

i.

j.

k.

l.

m.

n.

o.

p.

q.

r.

s.

t.

D. Generally Speaking Write each spelling word for the group it best fits.

1. wharf, dock, _____

2. prescription, treatment, _____

3. grip, grab, _____

4. contract, understanding, _____

5. persuade, win over, _____

6. equipment, tools, _____

7. go on, continue, _____

8. fuel, power, _____

9. unnecessary, unimportant, _____

10. got, accepted, _____

11. daily, monthly, _____

12. none, not any, _____

13. crawl, slide, _____

14. cousin, nephew, _____

15. talk, announcement, _____

16. criminal, burglar, _____

17. look, gaze, _____

18. short, quick, _____

19. guide, direct, _____

20. sadness, sorrow, _____

Spelling Words

creep	speech	squeeze	weekly	needless
proceed	agreement	peer	steer	brief
grief	thief	niece	pier	neither
received	energy	machinery	convince	medicine

E. Break the Code Use the code to write the spelling words.

a	b	c	d	e	f	g	h	i	j	k	l	m	n	o	p	q	r	s	t	u	v	w	x	y	z
↓	↓	↓	↓	↓	↓	↓	↓	↓	↓	↓	↓	↓	↓	↓	↓	↓	↓	↓	↓	↓	↓	↓	↓	↓	↓
q	e	o	j	v	s	a	g	p	y	i	x	b	r	c	h	t	d	m	z	w	k	l	f	n	u

1. qpkbx _____
2. fqbbn _____
3. sbrkokyb _____
4. ocyekyob _____
5. ybkqpbn _____
6. ybbrwbff _____
7. mnkbx _____
8. incobbr _____
9. ubbvwj _____
10. onbbi _____

11. ikbn _____
12. hnkbx _____
13. fibbop _____
14. fazbbtb _____
15. ibbn _____
16. bybnhxj _____
17. ykbob _____
18. sgopkybnj _____
19. nbobkebr _____
20. ghnbbsbyq _____

F. Sort Your _E_ Sounds Find the missing vowels and write the spelling words.

1. gr __ __ f _____
2. sp __ __ ch _____
3. n __ __ ther _____
4. st __ __ r _____
5. p __ __ r _____
6. p __ __ r _____
7. w __ __ kly _____
8. br __ __ f _____

9. cr __ __ p _____
10. th __ __ f _____
11. proc __ __ d _____
12. rec __ __ ved _____
13. n __ __ dless _____
14. n __ __ ce _____
15. squ __ __ ze _____
16. agr __ __ ment _____

G. Using Other Word Forms Write the Other Word Form (p. 32) that completes each series.

1. squeezes, squeezed, _____

2. creeps, _____ , creeping

3. convinces, convinced, _____

4. receives, received, _____

5. grieves, grieved, _____

H. Challenge Words Write the Challenge Word that completes each analogy.

preacher	sincere	honesty	immediate	preceded

1. **lie** is to **deceit** as **truth** is to _____

2. **school** is to **teacher** as **church** is to _____

3. **untruthful** is to **dishonest** as **genuine** is to _____

4. **after** is to **before** as **followed** is to _____

5. **slow** is to **fast** as **delayed** is to _____

I. Spelling and Writing Use as many of the Spelling Words, Other Word Forms, and Challenge Words as you can in sentences about one of the following titles. Then circle the spelling words you used. Proofread your spelling.

Return From an Ocean Adventure or Forgive and Forget

Example: *The cautious animal* (crept) *from the* (pier).

9

A. Pretest Write each spelling word.

B. Spelling Words and Phrases

1.	minor	minor or major
2.	silent	silent approval
3.	private	private property
4.	primary	primary colors
5.	horizon	beyond the horizon
6.	advice	good bit of advice
7.	polite	a polite greeting
8.	dislike	a strong dislike
9.	decline	will decline the offer
10.	inclined	inclined to agree
11.	unwise	unwise decision
12.	arrive	will arrive at five
13.	excitement	concealed their excitement
14.	admire	had to admire
15.	desire	to desire a new desk
16.	inquire	will inquire within
17.	umpire	the jumpy umpire
18.	entirely	entirely alone
19.	obey	tries to obey
20.	greater	lesser or greater

Other Word Forms

minors, minority
silently, silence
privately, privacy
prime, primaries
horizons, horizontal
advise, advising, adviser
politely, politeness
like, disliked, disliking
declined, declining
incline, inclining

wise, unwisely
arriving, arrival
excite, exciting
admiring, admirable
desiring, desirable
inquiring, inquiry
umpired, umpires
entire, entirety
obeyed, obeying
great, greatly

C. Visual Warm-up Write each word in its correct shape.

a.
b.
c.
d.
e.
f.
g.
h.
i.
j.
k.
l.
m.
n.
o.
p.
q.
r.
s.
t.

D. Sort Your Vowels

1. In alphabetical order, write the four spelling words that have the vowel sound of long *i* in the first syllable.

a. _____ c. _____

b. _____ d. _____

2. In alphabetical order, write the fourteen spelling words that have the vowel sound of long *i* in the second syllable. Include words in which *r* follows long *i*.

a. _____ f. _____ k. _____

b. _____ g. _____ l. _____

c. _____ h. _____ m. _____

d. _____ i. _____ n. _____

e. _____ j. _____

E. Word Search
The spelling words can be found in the word puzzle. The words appear across and down. Circle and write the words.

Across

1. _____

2. _____

3. _____

4. _____

5. _____

6. _____

7. _____

8. _____

9. _____

10. _____

11. _____

12. _____

```
d e c l i n e o m i n o r
i s d i n u n w i s e b z
s i l e n t g r e a t e r
l z p r i v a t e r h y m
i o p s t a d m i r e v w
k h o r i z o n b i l m i
e a l v n w w o b v a o n
d d i l q b s t u e v a c
e v t s u m p i r e t w l
s i e c i d d f g g h b i
i c n p r i m a r y m o n
r e s s e n t i r e l y e
e x c i t e m e n t a l d
```

Down

13. _____

14. _____

15. _____

16. _____

17. _____

18. _____

19. _____

20. _____

Spelling Words

minor	silent	private	primary	horizon
advice	polite	dislike	decline	inclined
unwise	arrive	excitement	admire	desire
inquire	umpire	entirely	obey	greater

F. Words and Meanings Write a spelling word for each meaning. Then read down each column to find three more spelling words.

1. a person who rules in sports   _ □ _ _ _ _

2. a suggestion about doing something   _ _ _ □ _

3. completely   _ _ _ □ _ _ _ _

4. showing good manners   _ _ _ □ _ _

5. to look at with wonder   _ _ _ _ □ _

6. foolish   _ _ _ _ □ _

7. to appear   _ _ _ _ □ _

8. willing or tending   _ _ _ _ □ _ _ _

9. not for public use   _ _ _ _ _ _ □

10. to ask about something   _ □ _ _ _ _ _

11. larger   _ _ _ _ □ _ _

12. to refuse politely   □ _ _ _ _ _ _

13. to do what one is told   _ _ □ _

14. to care little for   _ _ _ □ _ _ _

15. a line where earth and sky seem to meet   _ _ _ □ _ _ _

16. first in importance   _ _ _ □ _ _ _

17. enthusiasm   _ _ _ _ _ □ _ _ _ _

18. Write the three spelling words made by each set of boxes.

a. _____   **b.** _____   **c.** _____

G. Using Other Word Forms Write the Other Word Form (p. 36) that fits each group of words.

1. quietly, softly, _____ (silent)

2. stupidly, foolishly, _____ (unwise)

3. by yourself, personally, _____ (private)

4. courteously, considerately, _____ (polite)

5. wholeness, completeness, _____ (entirely)

H. Challenge Words Write the Challenge Word that completes each sentence.

assignment	designer	livestock	retirement	collide

1. When objects crash together, they _____ .

2. When the queen needs a new dress, she summons a _____ .

3. When the student does homework, he completes the _____ .

4. When ranchers raise steer, they raise _____ .

5. When a person receives a pension, she may be enjoying _____ .

I. Spelling and Writing Use as many of the Spelling Words, Other Word Forms and Challenge Words as you can to write newspaper headlines. Then circle the spelling words you used. Proofread your spelling.

Example: *President to* (*Arrive*) *in* (*Private*) *Jet*

10

A. Pretest Write each spelling word.

B. Spelling Words and Phrases

1. poultry — poultry farm
2. shoulder — injured my shoulder
3. source — our only source
4. journey — at the end of the journey
5. tournament — a soccer tournament
6. total — total defeat
7. noble — a noble gesture
8. notice — without notice
9. motion — an unsteady motion
10. groceries — bought the groceries
11. nowhere — nowhere but here
12. photograph — a family photograph
13. overflow — will overflow into the sewer
14. glory — shared the glory
15. porter — signaled the porter
16. normal — a normal temperature
17. foreign — a foreign country
18. important — not very important
19. continent — the continent of Africa
20. contribute — will contribute to charity

Other Word Forms

shouldered, shouldering	photographs,
sources	photography,
journeyed	photographer
tournaments	overflowed, overflowing
totaled, totaling, totally, totality	glories, glorify, glorious
	porters
nobler, noblest, nobly	normally, normality
notices, noticed, notable, noticing	foreigner
	importance
motions, motioned, motioning	continents
grocery	contributions

C. Visual Warm-up Write each word in its correct shape.

a.

b.

c.

d.

e.

f.

g.

h.

i.

j.

k.

l.

m.

n.

o.

p.

q.

r.

s.

t.

D. Sort Your O's In alphabetical order, write the spelling words where they belong.

Words with r-controlled o

1. _____
2. _____
3. _____
4. _____
5. _____

Words with ou

6. _____
7. _____
8. _____
9. _____
10. _____

Words with Long o

11. _____
12. _____
13. _____
14. _____

15. _____
16. _____
17. _____
18. _____

19. Write the two words that did not fit anywhere.

a. _____ b. _____

E. Generally Speaking Write each spelling word for the group it best fits.

1. wrist, elbow, _____
2. observe, see, _____
3. flood, spill, _____
4. strange, alien, _____
5. foods, supplies, _____
6. travel, voyage, _____
7. usual, regular, _____
8. fame, honor, _____
9. birds, chickens, _____
10. give, offer, _____

11. competition, contests, _____
12. land mass, country, _____
13. movement, action, _____
14. complete, entire, _____
15. start, beginning, _____
16. carrier, attendant, _____
17. generous, grand, _____
18. picture, snapshot, _____
19. serious, valuable, _____
20. no place, not anywhere, _____

Spelling Words

poultry	shoulder	source	journey	tournament
total	noble	notice	motion	groceries
nowhere	photograph	overflow	glory	porter
normal	foreign	important	continent	contribute

F. Crossword Puzzle Solve the puzzle by using all the words from the spelling list. Write the words. Check your answers in the **Spelling Dictionary**.

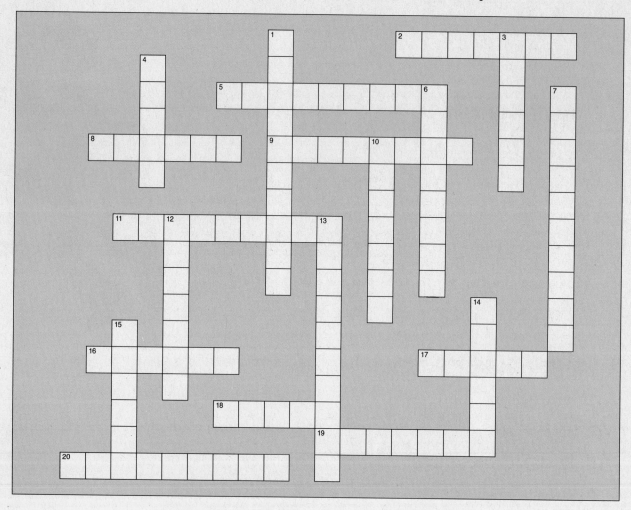

Across

2. a long trip

5. food items

8. a person who carries luggage

9. to spill over

11. not silly

16. the beginning

17. the full amount

18. a person of high rank

19. not anywhere

20. the largest piece of land

Down

1. a picture

3. usual

4. honor

6. a part of the body

7. to give

10. from another country

12. ducks, geese, and chickens

13. a series of contests

14. an important message

15. movement

G. Using Other Word Forms Write the Other Word Form (p. 40) that completes each sentence.

1. She took pictures. She was a _____ (photograph).

2. We were adding the numbers. We were _____ (total) the column of figures.

3. They traveled by horseback. They _____ (journey) on horses.

4. The weather was beautiful. It was a _____ (glory) day.

5. Wilfred lives in Germany. He is a _____ (foreign) visiting America.

H. Challenge Words Write the Challenge Word that replaces each underlined word or phrase.

bonus	corridor	origin	ignored	storage

1. They paid no attention to me. _____

2. The source of the river is Hudson Bay. _____

3. My unused furniture is in a warehouse. _____

4. I received the extra sum of money. _____

5. The hallway was crowded with guests. _____

I. Spelling and Writing Write each set of words in a sentence. You may use Other Word Forms. Proofread your spelling.

Example: porter – foreign – shoulder
The porter threw the foreign suitcase over his shoulder.

1. poultry – groceries – normal

2. continent – journey – glory

3. nowhere – total – tournament

4. important – source – photograph

5. overflow – contribute – notice

6. motion – noble

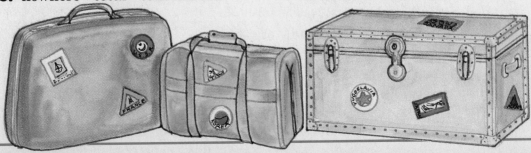

11

A. Pretest Write each spelling word.

B. Spelling Words and Phrases

1.	adventure	new adventure books
2.	natural	only natural food
3.	funeral	funeral march
4.	musical	musical chairs
5.	manual	the teacher's manual
6.	manufacturing	a manufacturing city
7.	rude	rude and crude
8.	include	does include tax
9.	introduce	can introduce my friend
10.	reduce	must reduce speed
11.	produce	will produce a product
12.	salute	to salute the flag
13.	cruel	cold, cruel winds
14.	truthful	always truthful
15.	through	through the woods
16.	proof	a proof of guilt
17.	gloomy	gloomy day
18.	jewels	stars like jewels
19.	screwdriver	a hammer and screwdriver
20.	tour	a four-week tour

Other Word Forms

adventures, adventurous
nature, naturally
funerals
music, musician
manuals, manually
manufacture,
  manufactured
rudest, rudely
included, including
introduced, introducing,
  introduction
reduced, reducing,
  reduction

produced, producing,
  production
saluted, saluting
crueler, cruelly, cruelty
truth, truthfully
prove, proving
gloom, gloomiest
jewel, jewelry
screwdrivers
toured, tourist

C. Visual Warm-up Write each word in its correct shape.

a.

b.

c.

d.

e.

f.

g.

h.

i.

j.

k.

l.

m.

n.

o.

p.

q.

r.

s.

t.

D. Sort Your *U*'s Decide where each spelling word belongs. Write the words. One word goes in more than one list.

Letter *u* in the First or Only Syllable

1. _____ 5. _____

2. _____ 6. _____

3. _____ 7. _____

4. _____

Letter *u* in the Third Syllable

16. _____

17. _____

Letter *u* in the Second Syllable

8. _____ 12. _____

9. _____ 13. _____

10. _____ 14. _____

11. _____ 15. _____

Words without the Letter *u*

18. _____

19. _____

20. _____

21. _____

E. Guide Words These word pairs are guide words that might appear in a dictionary. Write the words from the spelling list that would appear on the same page as each pair of guide words.

abandon – adventure

1. _____

concern – cushion

2. _____

favor – height

3. _____

4. _____

hesitate – insect

5. _____

insects – knowledge

6. _____

7. _____

labor – mining

8. _____

9. _____

minor – nowhere

10. _____

11. _____

power – refuse

12. _____

13. _____

14. _____

regard – sicken

15. _____

16. _____

17. _____

theater – various

18. _____

19. _____

20. _____

Spelling Words

adventure	natural	funeral	musical	manual
manufacturing	rude	include	introduce	reduce
produce	salute	cruel	truthful	through
proof	gloomy	jewels	screwdriver	tour

F. Careers Using words from the spelling list, complete each statement about various careers. Write the words.

1. Farmers would want their land to _____ healthy crops.

2. A police detective would insist on _____ .

3. A travel agent would plan a _____ .

4. A soldier would be expected to _____ .

5. A do-it-yourself repairer would read a _____ .

6. A composer might write a Broadway _____ .

7. A carpenter would require the use of a _____ .

8. An undertaker would direct plans for a _____ .

9. An environmentalist would work to keep the surroundings _____ .

10. A gem collector would deal in _____ .

G. Crossword Puzzle Solve the puzzle by using words from the spelling list. Write the words.

Across
2. honest
4. to present someone to another
8. to be part of a total

Down
1. dark and dim
3. not polite
5. finished
6. causing pain
7. to lessen

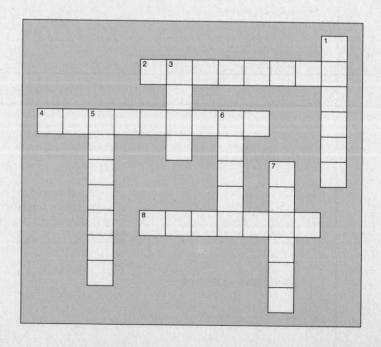

H. Using Other Word Forms Write the Other Word Form (p. 44) that completes each series.

1. produces, produced, _____

2. reduces, _____ , reducing

3. includes, included, _____

4. salutes, _____ , saluting

5. introduces, introduced, _____

I. Challenge Words Write the Challenge Word that completes each sentence.

accumulated	immune	fluid	cruising	rumors

1. You are _____ to this disease.

2. I have _____ many unusual stamps over the years.

3. The boat was _____ at a low speed.

4. Each liquid is also called a _____ .

5. Don't listen to silly _____ .

J. Spelling and Writing Use as many of the Spelling Words, Other Word Forms, and Challenge Words as you can in sentences about one of the following titles. Then circle the spelling words you used. Proofread your spelling.

How to Manufacture Rings at Low Cost or The Loss of a Pet

Example: *The new machine will* (reduce) *the need for* (screwdrivers).

REVIEWING LESSONS 7-11

■ raisin	★ thief	▲ squeeze	◆ tournament	○ groceries
shoulder	medicine	overflow	jewels	unpack
salute	notice	screwdriver	unwise	entertain
musical	exclaim	excitement	rascal	manual
umpire	obey	convince	agreement	polite

A. Cause and Effect Use Other Word Forms or the spelling words to complete the sentences. Write the words. The shape tells you in what column you can find the spelling word. If you need help, use the **Spelling Dictionary**.

1. Because I ▲ _____ the box, the ■ _____ were crushed.

2. Because the ○ _____ bag was too full, it ▲ _____ .

3. Because a band of ★ _____ stole the basketballs, all ◆ _____ were canceled.

4. Because the doctor ○ _____ the boxes quickly, the ★ _____ were saved.

5. Because the officer's ■ _____ were broken, ■ _____ the general was impossible.

6. Because one ■ _____ in the band was late, the ○ _____ was postponed.

7. Because the company's ○ _____ were outdated, the newest ▲ _____ were not illustrated.

8. Because you found the ◆ _____ , I cheered ▲ _____ .

9. Because I acted ◆ _____ , I was called a ◆ _____ .

10. Because they ★ _____ my weight loss, my parents ★ _____ , "Well done!"

11. Because the children ◆ _____ to behave, they ▲ _____ the teacher to let them read together.

12. Because the game was rained out, all the ■ _____ went home.

13. Because you behaved ★ _____ , I thanked you ○ _____ .

■ mass	★ raid	▲ claims	◆ explain	● contain
machinery	speech	photograph	received	nowhere
dislike	admire	cruel	greater	private
foreign	niece	poultry	neither	introduce
arrive	total	through	adventure	tour

B. Newspaper Headlines

Use Other Word Forms or the spelling words to complete the headlines. The shape tells you in what column you can find the spelling word. Write the words and capitalize each one. If you need help, use the **Spelling Dictionary**.

1. Giant Ants ★ _____ Picnic Last Night

2. Agitated Washing ■ _____ Overflow

3. ▲ _____ Farmers Scramble for Egg Business

4. Sea ◆ _____ Promise Whale of a Good Time

5. Jars ● _____ Peanut Butter Missing From Shelves

6. Students' ★ _____ Heard Today

7. Prevent ▲ _____ to Animals Week Planned

8. Dog ■ _____ Leash

9. Santa's Elves Meet ● _____ to Discuss Wages

10. Nephews and ★ _____ Search for Aunts and Uncles

11. Trapeze Artist ★ _____ for Hands and Feats

12. Jack ◆ _____ Award for Climbing Bean Stalk

13. Collectors Display ■ _____ Stamps

14. Cinderella ● _____ Glass Footwear

15. Denmark's Ruler Considered ◆ _____ Dane

16. Doctors ▲ _____ Cure for Common Cold

17. Train Finally ■ _____ on Time

18. Trips to ● _____ Advertised by Travel Agent

19. Facts Reveal ◆ _____ Hansel Nor Gretel Liked Gingerbread

20. Alice Reports Hare-raising Journey ▲ _____ Looking Glass

21. Number of Dwarves Found Whistling in Woods ★ _____ Seven

22. ▲ _____ Class Plans Exhibit

23. ● _____ Through Haunted Castles May Lift Spirits

24. Scientist ◆ _____ Why People Slurp

25. ■ _____ of People Jam Phone Booth

advice	exact	inquire	needless	reduce
bargain	glory	journey	noble	rude
brief	grief	margin	normal	standard
decline	horizon	minor	proceed	truthful
energy	important	natural	proof	vain

C. Break the Code

Use the code to write an Other Word Form for each spelling word.

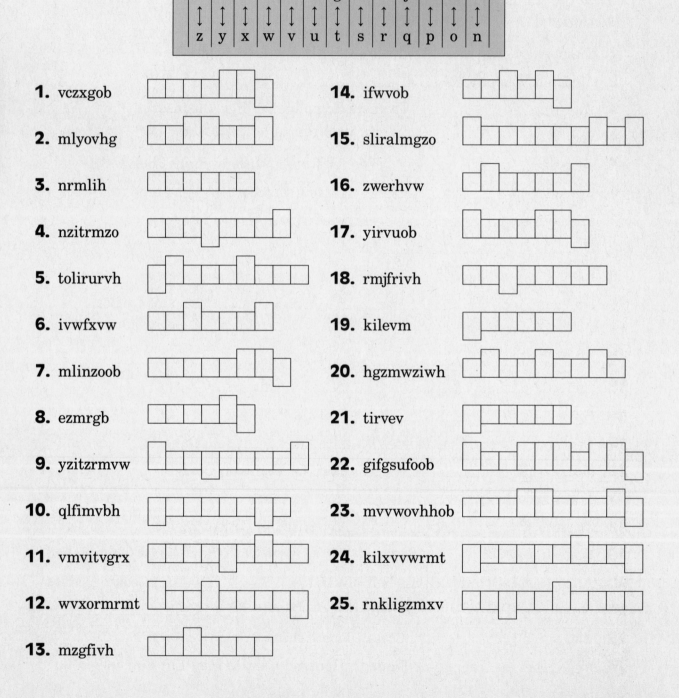

REVIEW

1. vczxgob
2. mlyovhg
3. nrmlih
4. nzitrmzo
5. tolirurvh
6. ivwfxvw
7. mlinzoob
8. ezmrgb
9. yzitzrmvw
10. qlfimvbh
11. vmvitvgrx
12. wvxormrmt
13. mzgfivh
14. ifwvob
15. sliralmgzo
16. zwerhvw
17. yirvuob
18. rmjfrivh
19. kilevm
20. hgzmwziwh
21. tirvev
22. gifgsufoob
23. mvvwovhhob
24. kilxvvwrmt
25. rnkligzmxv

attain	desire	include	pier	source
chamber	entirely	manufacturing	porter	staff
continent	funeral	motion	primary	steer
contribute	gloomy	obtain	produce	uncertain
creep	inclined	peer	silent	weekly

D. Word Arithmetic Perform one or two operations on each spelling word to write an Other Word Form.

1. creep + s = _____

2. source + s = _____

3. obtain + ing = _____

4. silent + ly = _____

5. funeral + s = _____

6. peer + ed = _____

7. attain + ing = _____

8. uncertain + ty = _____

9. desire + s = _____

10. porter + s = _____

11. produce + s = _____

12. contribute + s = _____

13. chamber + ed = _____

14. manufacturing − ing + ed = _____

15. steer + ing = _____

16. weekly − ly = _____

17. gloom − y = _____

18. pier + s = _____

19. motion + ed = _____

20. staff + ing = _____

21. primary − y + ies = _____

22. inclined − ed + ing = _____

23. continent + al = _____

24. entirely − ly + ty = _____

25. include − e + ing = _____

13

A. Pretest Write each spelling word.

B. Spelling Words and Phrases

1. acre — acre of swampland
2. labor — new labor unions
3. major — major effort
4. flavor — an improved flavor
5. favorite — favorite color
6. capable — capable carpenter
7. dangerous — a dangerous adventure
8. stranger — a total stranger
9. exchange — will exchange a shirt
10. arrangement — flower arrangement
11. invitation — invitation to lunch
12. operation — a minor operation
13. observation — observation tower
14. radiation — the sun's radiation
15. transportation — public transportation
16. stationary — a stationary target
17. area — picnic area
18. solo — solo flight
19. echo — hollow echo
20. volcano — erupting volcano

Other Word Forms

acres, acreage	operate, operating,
labored, laboring, laborer	operations,
majored, majority	operator
flavors, flavorful	observe, observant
favor, favoring	radiate, radiating
capably	transport,
danger, dangerously	transported
strange, strangely, strangeness	areas
exchanged, exchanging	solos, soloist
arrange, arranges, arranging	echoes
invited, inviting	volcanoes, volcanic

C. Visual Warm-up Write each word in its correct shape.

a.
b.
c.
d.
e.
f.
g.
h.
i.
j.
k.
l.
m.
n.
o.
p.
q.
r.
s.
t.

D. Crossword Puzzle Solve the puzzle by using all the words from the spelling list. Write the words. Check your answers in the **Spelling Dictionary**.

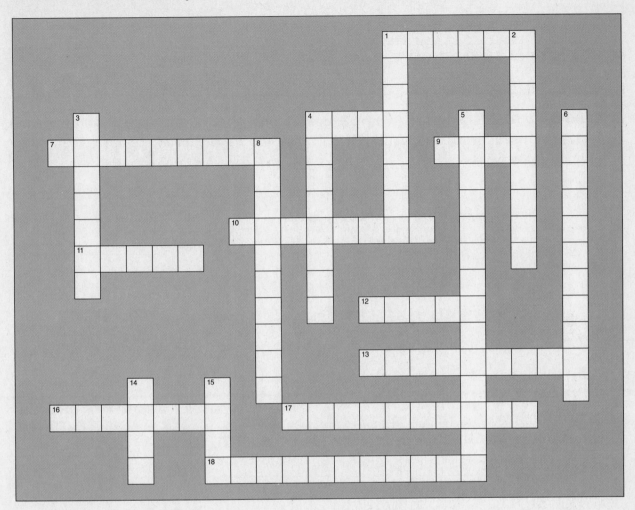

Across

1. to give a taste to
4. a repeated sound
7. unsafe
9. a flat, open space
10. an unknown person
11. work
12. an army officer
13. a heart transplant
16. a fiery mountain
17. a request to attend a party
18. something seen

Down

1. best-liked
2. the process of giving off energy
3. able
4. to trade for something else
5. planes, buses, and trains
6. the way something is put in order
8. not moving
14. a measure of land
15. alone

Spelling Words

acre	labor	major	flavor
favorite	capable	dangerous	stranger
exchange	arrangement	invitation	operation
observation	radiation	transportation	stationary
area	solo	echo	volcano

E. Guide Words These word pairs are guide words that might appear in a dictionary. Write the words from the spelling list that would appear on the same page as each pair of guide words.

abandon – adventure

1. _____

advertise – assign

2. _____
3. _____

boiler – chalk

4. _____

customer – design

5. _____

doubt – estate

6. _____

evil – fault

7. _____

favor – future

8. _____
9. _____

insects – knowledge

10. _____

labor – machine

11. _____

machinery – mining

12. _____

obey – percent

13. _____
14. _____

punctual – refuse

15. _____

silent – staff

16. _____

standard – succeed

17. _____
18. _____

theater – treat

19. _____

vary – wrench

20. _____

F. Using Other Word Forms Add an ending to each word to write an Other Word Form (p. 52).

1. operate + ing = _____

2. exchange + ing = _____

3. invite + ing = _____

4. radiate + ing = _____

5. arrange + ing = _____

6. What letter gets subtracted in the first four words? _____

G. Challenge Words Write the Challenge Word that completes each group of words.

dominated	domain	beige	proposal	reservation

1. brown, tan, _____

2. outline, plan, _____

3. condition, provision, _____

4. province, territory, _____

5. controlled, directed, _____

H. Spelling and Writing Write each set of words in a sentence. You may use Other Word Forms. Proofread your spelling.

Example: capable–dangerous-operation
He was capable of performing dangerous operations.

1. flavor—favorite—observation

2. solo—stranger—labor

3. major—volcano—acre

4. radiation—area—echo

5. invitation—arrangement—exchange

6. stationary—transportation

14

A. Pretest Write each spelling word.

B. Spelling Words and Phrases

1. plank — an oak plank
2. sprang — sprang higher
3. scratch — won't scratch the itch
4. scramble — had to scramble down
5. glance — a glance backward
6. advance — advance notice
7. balance — will balance the scales
8. damage — free from damage
9. manage — will manage to finish
10. command — giving a command
11. gallop — began to gallop
12. wrapped — was wrapped in foil
13. planned — planned a picnic
14. manner — a careful manner
15. scatter — will scatter seeds
16. frankly — frankly speaking
17. lasting — lasting friendship
18. landlord — paid the landlord
19. practice — to practice the piano
20. plunge — will plunge into water

Other Word Forms

planks	wrap, wrapping
spring, sprung	plan, planning
scratched, scratching	mannered
scrambled, scrambling	scattered, scattering
glanced, glancing	frank, frankest
advanced, advancing	last, lasted
balanced, balancing	landlords
damaged, damaging	practiced, practicing,
managed, managing	practically
commanded, commanding	plunged, plunging
galloped, galloping	

C. Visual Warm-up Write each word in its correct shape.

a.
b.
c.
d.
e.
f.
g.
h.
i.
j.
k.
l.
m.
n.
o.
p.
q.
r.
s.
t.

D. All in a Row Write the twenty spelling words in alphabetical order. Then join the boxed letters and write four hidden words.

1. a d v a n c e
2. b a l a n c e
3. c o m m a n d
4. d a m a g e
5. f r a n k l y
6. Hidden Word: vandal

7. g a l l o p
8. g l a n c e
9. l a n d l o r d
10. l a s t i n g
11. m a n a g e
12. Hidden Word: opening

13. m a n n e r
14. p l a n k
15. p l a n n e d
16. p l u n g e
17. p r a c t i c e
18. Hidden Word: manner

19. s c a t t e r
20. s c r a m b l e
21. s c r a t c h
22. s p r a n g
23. w r a p p e d
24. Hidden Word: scrap

E. Finding Words The words in the spelling list appear in the beginning (A-H), middle (I-Q), or end (R-Z) of the **Spelling Dictionary**. Write each word.

Beginning A-H

1. advance
2. balance
3. command
4. damage
5. frankly
6. gallop
7. glance

Middle I-Q

8. landlord
9. lasting
10. manage
11. manner
12. plank
13. planned
14. plunge
15. practice

End R-Z

16. scatter
17. scramble
18. scratch
19. sprang
20. wrapped

Spelling Words

plank	sprang	scratch	scramble	glance
advance	balance	damage	manage	command
gallop	wrapped	planned	manner	scatter
frankly	lasting	landlord	practice	plunge

F. Word Building The words below can all be used as verbs. Add the suffixes *ed* and *ing* to build two new words for each spelling word. Write the words.

Base Words	ed Words	ing Words
1. scratch	scratched	scratching
2. plunge	plunged	plunging
3. plan	planned	planning
4. glance	glanced	glancing
5. advance	advanced	advancing
6. balance	balanced	balancing
7. damage	damaged	damaging
8. manage	managed	managing
9. scramble	scrambled	scrambling
10. command	commanded	commanding
11. scatter	scattered	scattering
12. gallop	galloped	galloping
13. practice	practiced	practicing
14. wrap	wrapped	wrapping

G. Generally Speaking Write a spelling word for the group it best fits.

1. continuing, remaining, _lasting_
2. leaped, jumped, _sprang_
3. way, style, _manner_
4. board, lumber, _plank_
5. renter, owner, _landlord_
6. openly, honestly, _frankly_

H. Using Other Word Forms Write the Other Word Form (p. 56) that rhymes with each word pair.

1. gambling, rambling, _scrambling_ (scramble)
2. shattered, splattered, _scattered_ (scatter)
3. hung, strung, _sprung_ (sprang)
4. prancing, romancing, _advancing_ (advance)
5. patched, thatched, _scratched_ (scratch)

I. Challenge Words Write the Challenge Word that completes each phrase.

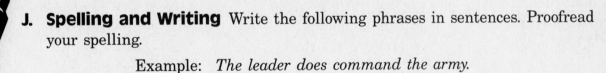

navigator	scampered	antique	amateur	examine

1. scurried and _scampered_
2. investigate and _examine_
3. beginner and _amateur_
4. sailor and _navigator_
5. old-fashioned and _antique_

J. Spelling and Writing Write the following phrases in sentences. Proofread your spelling.

Example: *The leader does command the army.*

1. does <u>command</u> the army
2. to <u>damage</u> the car
3. will <u>gallop</u> away
4. sudden <u>advance</u>
5. new <u>landlord</u>
6. expressed herself <u>frankly</u>
7. hours of <u>practice</u>
8. strange <u>manner</u>
9. off <u>balance</u>
10. a deep <u>plunge</u>

11. broken <u>plank</u>
12. <u>planned</u> an escape
13. couldn't <u>scramble</u> over
14. will <u>scatter</u> seeds
15. to <u>glance</u> down the street
16. <u>sprang</u> up
17. <u>wrapped</u> around
18. might <u>scratch</u> the table
19. couldn't <u>manage</u>
20. was <u>lasting</u>

15

A. Pretest Write each spelling word.

B. Spelling Words and Phrases

1. weave — to spin and <u>weave</u>
2. league — a minor <u>league</u> team
3. breathe — to <u>breathe</u> deeply
4. speaker — today's <u>speaker</u>
5. creature — a weird <u>creature</u>
6. treatment — silent <u>treatment</u>
7. defeat — a win or a <u>defeat</u>
8. retreat — will <u>retreat</u> from danger
9. beneath — <u>beneath</u> the sea
10. appeal — an <u>appeal</u> for help
11. disease — a <u>disease</u> spread by fleas
12. release — can <u>release</u> the balloon
13. increase — an <u>increase</u> in allowance
14. theater — a movie <u>theater</u>
15. realizes — <u>realizes</u> they're lazy
16. meant — <u>meant</u> no harm
17. measure — a teaspoon <u>measure</u>
18. pleasure — a <u>pleasure</u> to serve you
19. jealous — a <u>jealous</u> student
20. search — to <u>search</u> the beach

Other Word Forms

weaved, weaving
leagues
breathes, breathed,
  breathing
speak, spoke, speech
creatures
treat, treatments
defeated, defeating
retreated, retreating
appealing
diseased

released, releasing
increased, increasing
theaters
realize, realizing,
  realization
mean, meaning
measures, measured,
  measuring
pleasures, pleasurable
jealousy
searches, searching

C. Visual Warm-up Write each word in its correct shape.

a.
b.
c.
d.
e.
f.
g.
h.
i.
j.
k.
l.
m.
n.
o.
p.
q.
r.
s.
t.

D. Sort Your Words Each of the words in the spelling list has an *ea* combination. Write the fifteen words that have a long *e* sound. Then write the four words that have a short *e* sound.

Words with a Long *e* Sound		Words with a Short *e* Sound
1. weave	9. _____	16. _____
2. league	10. _____	17. _____
3. breathe	11. _____	18. _____
4. _____	12. _____	19. _____
5. _____	13. _____	
6. _____	14. _____	
7. _____	15. _____	
8. _____		

E. Guide Words These word pairs are guide words that might appear in a dictionary. Write the words from the spelling list that would appear on the same page as each pair of guide words.

advertise – boil
1. appeal
2. beneath

boiler – chalk
3. breathe

concern – document
4. creature
5. defeat
6. disease

hesitate – knowledge
7. increase
8. jealous

labor – machine
9. league

machinery – mining
10. meant
11. measure

perform – refuse
12. pleasure
13. realizes

regard – sicken
14. retreat
15. release
16. search

silent – staff
17. speaker

theater – treat
18. theater

treatment – wrench
19. treatment
20. weave

Spelling Words

weave	league	breathe	speaker	creature
treatment	defeat	retreat	beneath	appeal
disease	release	increase	theater	realizes
meant	measure	pleasure	jealous	search

F. Be a Sentence Detective Unscramble the word under each blank. Write each unscrambled word.

1. The senator made an ___appeal___ for an ___increase___ in taxes.
   leappa   crinsaee

2. I ___meant___ to sign up for the bowling ___league___ yesterday.
   aemnt   ueglae

3. The angry ___speaker___ made a demand for the immediate
   keespar
   ___release___ of the prisoners.
   reelsea

4. The doctor thought the ___treatment___ would cure the ___disease___.
   teamnttre   seedsia

5. ___Beneath___ the apple tree we could ___breathe___ in the
   theenab   theeabr
   sweet odors.

6. The monstrous ___creature___ was ___jealous___ of its rival.
   trueeacr   aejouls

7. When an army ___realizes___ it is losing, it plans a ___retreat___.
   zealsier   ateertr

8. Be sure to ___measure___ your amount of wool before you
   seemaur
   ___weave___ on the loom.
   veewa

9. The baby-sitter was making a ___search___ for things to give
   rcheas
   ___pleasure___ to the children.
   seeauplr

10. The movie in the ___theater___ showed the hero overcoming a recent
    tearthe
    ___defeat___.
    tafede

G. Using Other Word Forms Write the Other Word Form (p. 60) that replaces each underlined word or phrase.

1. There are five groups of teams in our division. _leagues_ (league)
2. Her salary became larger last month. _increased_ (increase)
3. Thousands of balloons were let go. _released_ (release)
4. The cat is moving away from the angry dog. _retreating_ (retreat)
5. Our team beat the champions. _defeated_ (defeat)

H. Challenge Words Write the Challenge Word that fits each group of words.

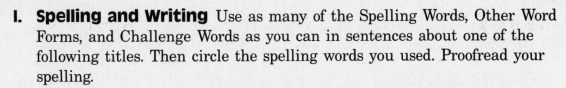

unfriendly	encyclopedia	energetic	preference	vehicle

1. book, reference, volume, _encyclopedia_
2. choice, selection, desire, _preference_
3. unkind, suspicious, hostile, _unfriendly_
4. automobile, transportation, bus, _vehicle_
5. fitness, work out, vigorous, _energetic_

I. Spelling and Writing Use as many of the Spelling Words, Other Word Forms, and Challenge Words as you can in sentences about one of the following titles. Then circle the spelling words you used. Proofread your spelling.

Alone, Pursued, Rescued and The Contest

Example: *When the ⟨search⟩ finally ended, I ⟨breathed⟩ a sigh of relief.*

16

A. Pretest Write each spelling word.

B. Spelling Words and Phrases

1. **highly** — highly explosive
2. **slight** — a slight error
3. **frighten** — couldn't frighten me
4. **delightfully** — a delightfully cool breeze
5. **twilight** — twilight shadows
6. **height** — height of eight feet
7. **diameter** — diameter of the circle
8. **bicycle** — the stolen bicycle
9. **satisfied** — a satisfied customer
10. **design** — to draw a design
11. **stylish** — stylish suit
12. **typewriter** — typewriter keyboard
13. **rinse** — to rinse or wash
14. **width** — narrow width
15. **midst** — midst the crowd
16. **knitting** — knitting and sewing
17. **trimmed** — cut and trimmed
18. **slither** — to slither away
19. **system** — computer system
20. **mystery** — weird mystery story

Other Word Forms

high, highest
slightly, slightest
fright, frightened,
 frightening
delight, delighted,
 delightful
twilights
heights
diameters
bicycles, bicycling
satisfy, satisfies,
 satisfying, satisfaction

designed, designer
style, styling, stylishly
typewriters, typewritten
rinsed, rinsing
widths
mid, middle
knit, knitted
trim, trimming
slithers, slithered,
 slithering
systems
mysteries, mysterious

C. Visual Warm-up Write each word in its correct shape.

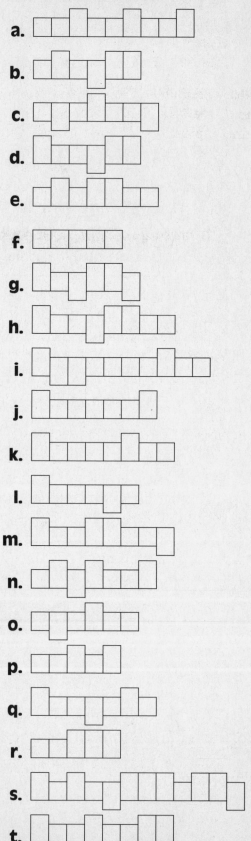

a.
b.
c.
d.
e.
f.
g.
h.
i.
j.
k.
l.
m.
n.
o.
p.
q.
r.
s.
t.

D. The I's Have It All the spelling words have either a long or a short *i* sound. Write each spelling word where it belongs. A word may go in more than one list.

Short *i* Sound Spelled *i*

1. _____
2. _____
3. _____
4. _____
5. _____
6. _____
7. _____
8. _____

Short *i* Sound Spelled *e*

12. _____
13. _____
14. _____

Long *i* Sound Spelled *i*

15. _____
16. _____
17. _____
18. _____
19. _____
20. _____
21. _____
22. _____
23. _____

Long *i* Sound Spelled *y*

24. _____
25. _____

Long *i* Sound Spelled *ei*

26. _____

Long *i* Sound Spelled *ie*

27. _____

Short *i* Sound Spelled *y*

9. _____
10. _____
11. _____

E. Phrase Clues Use a spelling word to complete each phrase. Write the words.

1. _____ needles
2. solved the _____
3. _____ suspicious
4. length and _____
5. electric _____
6. _____ and weight
7. traced the _____
8. didn't _____ me
9. a _____ coat
10. _____ his beard

11. _____ their hunger
12. in the _____ of the crowd
13. only a _____ breeze
14. long shadows of _____
15. a _____ refreshing swim
16. will _____ the dishes
17. _____ of the circle
18. rode on the _____ path
19. a communications _____
20. did _____ across the road

Spelling Words

highly	slight	frighten	delightfully	twilight
height	diameter	bicycle	design	satisfied
stylish	typewriter	rinse	width	midst
knitting	trimmed	slither	system	mystery

F. Break the Code Use the code to write the spelling words.

a	b	c	d	e	f	g	h	i	j	k	l	m	n	o	p	q	r	s	t	u	v	w	x	y	z
↓	↓	↓	↓	↓	↓	↓	↓	↓	↓	↓	↓	↓	↓	↓	↓	↓	↓	↓	↓	↓	↓	↓	↓	↓	↓
g	d	z	r	u	e	y	w	k	a	c	p	s	h	b	n	l	m	f	v	t	x	q	o	j	i

1. nfzanu _____

2. bfmzap _____

3. bfqzanuseqqg _____

4. uhzqzanu _____

5. mqzanu _____

6. sdzanufp _____

7. bzjrfufd _____

8. ozkgkqf _____

9. rgmufdg _____

10. rzbmu _____

11. hzbun _____

12. udzrrfb _____

13. mqzunfd _____

14. mjuzmszfb _____

15. mgmufr _____

16. mugqzmn _____

17. ipzuuzpa _____

18. nzanqg _____

19. uglfhdzufd _____

20. dzpmf _____

G. Be a Word Doctor Write the one operation you must perform before adding the suffix to each word. Write the new word.

	Operations		New Words
Example: skim	*double the* m	+ ed =	*skimmed*
1. mystery	_____	+ ous =	_____
2. trim	_____	+ ed =	_____
3. knit	_____	+ ing =	_____
4. typewrite	_____	+ er =	_____
5. style	_____	+ ish =	_____

H. Using Other Word Forms Write the Other Word Form (p. 64) that completes each series.

1. delights, _____ , delighting

2. bicycles, bicycled, _____

3. frightens, _____ , frightening

4. styles, styled, _____

5. _____ , satisfied, satisfying

I. Challenge Words Write the Challenge Word that completes each phrase.

guilty	dynamite	judicial	liberal	vanilla

1. not chocolate, but _____

2. not innocent, but _____

3. not legislative, but _____

4. not gunpowder, but _____

5. not conservative, but _____

J. Spelling and Writing Write in your journal. Use as many of the Spelling Words, Other Word Forms, and Challenge Words as you can to write a page about the night you and your friends were scared out of your wits. Then circle the spelling words you used. Remember when writing a journal to include the date, the time, and what happened. Proofread your spelling.

Example: *January 6–7:00—I tore my* (knitted) *shirt with the* (stylish) (trim).

17

A. Pretest Write each spelling word.

B. Spelling Words and Phrases

1.	term	school term
2.	nerve	the nerve to try
3.	serve	a poor serve
4.	servant	hired another servant
5.	permanent	left a permanent mark
6.	personal	personal belongings
7.	deserve	deserve one more chance
8.	dessert	fruit for dessert
9.	reverse	can reverse the order
10.	terror	filled with terror
11.	territory	the animal's territory
12.	terrible	terrible mistake
13.	berry	a nut or a berry
14.	buried	buried in the garden
15.	computer	computer programmer
16.	curve	curve in the road
17.	furnace	a hot furnace
18.	surface	swam to the surface
19.	purchase	will purchase a gift
20.	purpose	forgot the purpose

Other Word Forms

terms, termed
nerves, nervous
serves, served, serving,
  servants
permanently
person, personally,
  personality
deserves, deserved,
  deserving
desserts
reverses, reversing, reversal
terrors

territories, territorial
terribly
berries
bury, buries, burying
compute, computers
curves, curved, curving
furnaces
surfaces, surfacing
purchases, purchased,
  purchasing
purposes, purposely,
  purposeful

C. Visual Warm-up Write each word in its correct shape.

a.

b.

c.

d.

e.

f.

g.

h.

i.

j.

k.

l.

m.

n.

o.

p.

q.

r.

s.

t.

D. _Er_ or _Ur_ The letters _er_ and _ur_ often have the same sound. List the spelling words in alphabetical order. Put a wavy line under the words spelled with _er._ Circle the words spelled with _ur._ Put an **X** before the four words in which _er_ does not have the sound as in _burn_ or _fern._

1. _____
2. _____
3. _____
4. _____
5. _____
6. _____
7. _____

8. _____
9. _____
10. _____
11. _____
12. _____
13. _____
14. _____

15. _____
16. _____
17. _____
18. _____
19. _____
20. _____

E. Generally Speaking Write each of the spelling words for the group it best fits.

1. area, region, _____
2. arc, bend, _____
3. butler, maid, _____
4. wait on, work for, _____
5. ice cream, pie, _____
6. sell, buy, _____
7. machine, calculator, _____
8. fear, horror, _____
9. stove, heater, _____
10. earn, worthy of, _____
11. covered, put under, _____
12. courage, strong will, _____
13. lasting, won't wear out, _____
14. change direction, backward, _____
15. length of time, school session, _____
16. rise to the top, outside layer, _____
17. private, one's own, _____

18. awful, bad, _____
19. fruit, grape, _____
20. reason, goal, _____

Spelling Words

	term	*nerve*	*serve*	*servant*	*permanent*
	personal	*deserve*	*dessert*	*reverse*	*terror*
	territory	*terrible*	*berry*	*buried*	*computer*
	curve	*furnace*	*surface*	*purchase*	*purpose*

F. Finding Words The words in the spelling list appear in the beginning (A-H), middle (I-Q), or end (R-Z) of the **Spelling Dictionary**. Write each word.

**Beginning
A-H**

1. _____

2. _____

3. _____

4. _____

5. _____

6. _____

7. _____

**Middle
I-Q**

8. _____

9. _____

10. _____

11. _____

12. _____

**End
R-Z**

13. _____

14. _____

15. _____

16. _____

17. _____

18. _____

19. _____

20. _____

G. Using Other Word Forms Write the Other Word Form (p. 68) that completes each clue.

1. people paid to care for others _____ (servant)

2. uneasy or restless _____ (nerve)

3. rounded or shaped like an arc _____ (curve)

4. types of fruit _____ (berry)

5. lands or regions _____ (territory)

H. Challenge Words Write the Challenge Word that completes each phrase.

conservation	conversion	detergent	eternal	occurred

1. either soap or _____

2. either forever or _____

3. either happened or _____

4. either changeover or _____

5. either preservation or _____

I. Spelling and Writing Use as many of the Spelling Words, Other Word Forms, and Challenge Words as you can in sentences about one of the following titles. Then circle the spelling words you used. Proofread your spelling.

A Long Walk Back or Just One More Time

Example: *The (nervous) pirates finally found the (buried) treasure.*

18 REVIEWING LESSONS 13-17

■ frighten ★ bicycle ▲ stranger ◆ echo ● mystery
dangerous bury breathe terror area
scratch scramble slither search observation
plunge territory planned creature height
realizes measure reverse deserve sprang

A. Story Time Choose Other Word Forms or the spelling words to complete the sentences. Write the words. The shape tells you in what column you can find the spelling word. Write each word or its Other Word Form only once. If you need help, use the **Spelling Dictionary**.

The Buried Treasure

One day after school, we found two ● **(1.)** _____ notes left on our

★ **(2.)** _____ . The notes told us where to find

★ **(3.)** _____ treasure. Immediately, we pedaled off to the mountain,

the first of the two ● **(4.)** _____ described in the notes. We felt a bit

■ **(5.)** _____ wondering what ■ **(6.)** _____ lay ahead.

From the mountaintop, we ● **(7.)** _____ the sun going down. Though

not usually afraid of ● **(8.)** _____ , we were indeed frightened by the

▲ **(9.)** _____ of the area. Then we heard a voice that shrieked and

◆ **(10.)** _____ . We went ● **(11.)** _____ to our feet, and

then we ★ **(12.)** _____ down the mountain to the valley.

After ■ **(13.)** _____ an itch on my foot, I ■ **(14.)** _____

into a pool of cold water and lost my ▲ **(15.)** _____ . After this brief

moment of ◆ **(16.)** _____ , I ■ **(17.)** _____ that I still

wanted to keep ◆ **(18.)** _____ for the marked

★ **(19.)** _____ .

Suddenly, several furry ◆ **(20.)** _____ that

★ **(21.)** _____ eight feet in height stood in our way. Trembling, we

crouched down and ▲ **(22.)** _____ through the grass, changing our

▲ **(23.)** _____ and ▲ **(24.)** _____ our direction.

To our surprise, we backed into the two sticks marking the buried treasure. After

our long search, we felt we ◆ **(25.)** _____ the treasure.

72 Review—Lesson 18

■ wrapped	★ plank	▲ operation	◆ dessert	● acre
servant	invitation	speaker	practice	trimmed
solo	theater	furnace	meant	league
beneath	design	midst	knitting	gallop
typewriter	purchase	manner	volcano	computer

B. Out of the Ordinary Days Decide how to complete each title with Other Word Forms or the spelling words. Write the words. The shape tells you in what column you can find the spelling word. Capitalize each word.

Example: Present ■ _____*Wrapping*_____ Day

1. Plow Forty ● _____ Day

2. Hair ● _____ Day

3. ▲ _____ on a Doctor Day

4. ■ _____ One Helping of Vegetables Day

5. Eat Delicious ◆ _____ Day

6. Spare All Bowling ● _____ Day

7. Wear Earmuffs on Guest ▲ _____ Day

8. Forget ◆ _____ the Piano Day

9. Nail the ★ _____ Together Day

10. ★ _____ a Pet to Dinner Day

11. Sing Two ■ _____ in the Shower Day

12. Ride ● _____ Horses Day

13. Hide ■ _____ the Stairs Day

14. Visit Four Movie ★ _____ Day

15. Say What You ◆ _____ Day

16. Tap on Ten Tiny ■ _____ Day

17. Buy Needles for ◆ _____ Day

18. Fix Flaming ▲ _____ Day

19. Debug All ● _____ Day

20. Eat Only the ▲ _____ of Your Sandwich Day

21. Draw Dotted ★ _____ Day

22. View a ◆ _____ Eruption Day

23. Mind Your ▲ _____ Day

24. Return Unwanted ★ _____ Day

favorite	arrangement	radiation	transportation	flavor
command	balance	advance	damage	manage
treatment	retreat	defeat	appeal	weave
satisfied	delightfully	stylish	width	highly
curve	surface	purpose	terrible	serve

C. Word Building Add word parts to each spelling word or its base word to make Other Word Forms. Write the words.

Spelling Words	s or es	ed	ing
Example: wave	*waves*	*waved*	*waving*
1. flavor			
2. command			
3. balance			
4. retreat			
5. damage			
6. favorite			
7. arrangement			
8. radiation			
9. transportation			
10. manage			
11. treatment			
12. advance			
13. defeat			
14. appeal			
15. weave			
16. delightfully			
17. stylish			
18. curve			
19. surface			
20. serve			
21. satisfied			
22. purpose			
23. width			

Write Other Word Forms for each spelling word below.

24. highly _____ _____

25. terrible _____ _____

■ major   ★ labor   ▲ capable   ◆ exchange   ● stationary
frankly   lasting   glance   scatter   landlord
disease   increase   release   pleasure   jealous
slight   twilight   diameter   system   rinse
term   nerve   buried   permanent   personal

D. Words in a Series Use Other Word Forms or the spelling words to complete each series. Write the words. The shape tells you in what column you can find the spelling word. Use each word or its Other Word Form only once.

1. working, toiling, ★ _____

2. trading, swapping, ◆ _____

3. unmoving, motionless, ● _____

4. captains, colonels, ■ _____

5. exists, continues, ★ _____

6. able, qualified, ▲ _____

7. sprinkling, throwing about, ◆ _____

8. gaining, growing, ★ _____

9. owners, renters, ● _____

10. envy, suspicion, ● _____

11. sincere, truthful, ■ _____

12. delights, joys, ◆ _____

13. dusk, nightfall, ★ _____

14. washing lightly, spraying, ● _____

15. looking, staring, ▲ _____

16. methods, plans, ◆ _____

17. untied, freed, ▲ _____

18. sicknesses, ailments, ■ _____

19. circle, radius, ▲ _____

20. lastingly, enduringly, ◆ _____

21. least, smallest, ■ _____

22. times, school periods, ■ _____

23. hide, cover up, ▲ _____

24. courageous, brave, ★ _____

25. individual, human being, ● _____

19

A. Pretest Write each spelling word.

B. Spelling Words and Phrases

1. spare — a spare tire
2. stare — will dare you to stare
3. carefully — carefully wrapped
4. warehouse — a stocked warehouse
5. declare — may declare war
6. prepare — to prepare a report
7. farewell — said their farewell
8. scarcely — scarcely aware
9. various — in various stages
10. armor — the knight's armor
11. article — a newspaper article
12. argument — a no-win argument
13. starve — would rather starve
14. garbage — garbage collection
15. charming — a charming manner
16. regard — without regard
17. department — the art department
18. charity — charity work
19. sheriff — deputy sheriff
20. favorable — a favorable choice

Other Word Forms

spared, sparing, sparingly
stares, staring
care, careful
warehouses
declared, declaring,
   declaration
prepared, preparing,
   preparation
farewells
scarce, scarcity
vary, varying
armors, armory
articles
argue, argued, arguing
starves, starving,
   starvation
charm, charmed
regards, regarded
departments,
   departmental
charities
sheriffs
favor, favorite

C. Visual Warm-up Write each word in its correct shape.

a.
b.
c.
d.
e.
f.
g.
h.
i.
j.
k.
l.
m.
n.
o.
p.
q.
r.
s.
t.

D. StARt to StARe Eighteen spelling words have an *ar* combination. Write each *ar* spelling word where it belongs.

ar as in *far*
1. _____
2. _____
3. _____
4. _____
5. _____
6. _____
7. _____
8. _____

ar as in *fare* or *carry*	
9. _____	14. _____
10. _____	15. _____
11. _____	16. _____
12. _____	17. _____
13. _____	18. _____

19. Write the two words that did not fit in either list.

a. _____   **b.** _____

E. Word Search The spelling words can be found in the word puzzle. The words appear across, down, and diagonally. Circle and write the words.

Across

1. _____
2. _____
3. _____
4. _____
5. _____
6. _____
7. _____
8. _____
9. _____
10. _____

```
m s p a r e s g o l m d
a r m o r s t a r v e e
r r o r e g a r d p r p
t i g a b c r b d e f a
i v m u z z e a f f t r
c h a r m i n g a a c t
l c h r p e q e r v h m
e d d p i h n t e o a e
x o r r m o t t w r r n
w a r e h o u s e a i t
b l l p r e t s l b t p
d n c a r e f u l l y r
s c a r c e l y l e e t
a s h e r i f f e r m t
d e c l a r e t m o t s
```

Down

11. _____
12. _____
13. _____
14. _____
15. _____
16. _____
17. _____
18. _____

Diagonally

19. _____
20. _____

Spelling Words

spare	stare	carefully	warehouse	declare
prepare	farewell	scarcely	various	armor
article	argument	starve	garbage	charming
regard	department	charity	sheriff	favorable

F. Words and Meanings Write a spelling word for each meaning. Then read down each column to find one spelling word and one Other Word Form (p. 76).

1. barely   _ _ _ _ ☐ _ _ _ _

2. aid to the poor   _ ☐ _ _ _ _ _

3. to make ready for a purpose   _ _ _ _ ☐ _ _ _

4. consideration or careful thought   ☐ _ _ _ _ _

5. a body covering worn in battle   _ _ ☐ _ _ _

6. a written story on a specific subject   _ _ _ _ ☐ _ _

7. a disagreement   _ _ _ _ _ _ ☐ _

8. anything worthless   ☐ _ _ _ _ _

9. a good-bye   _ _ _ _ ☐ _ _ _

10. to state publicly   _ _ _ _ ☐ _ _

11. cautiously   _ _ _ ☐ _ _ _ _

12. extra   _ _ _ _ ☐

13. a county's chief law officer   _ _ ☐ _ _ _ _

14. positive or pleasing   _ _ _ ☐ _ _ _ _

15. different   _ _ _ _ ☐ _ _

16. to die due to hunger   ☐ _ _ _ _

17. a division or part   _ _ ☐ _ _ _ _ _ _

18. to look long at   ☐ _ _ _ _

19. Write the spelling word and the Other Word Form made by the sets of boxes.

   a. _____   **b.** _____

G. Using Other Word Forms Write the Other Word Form (p. 76) that completes each sentence.

1. A statement is a _____ (declare).

2. Something done beforehand is a _____ (prepare).

3. Discussing opposite points of view is _____ (argument).

4. Organizations helping those in need are called _____ (charity).

5. Looking long and directly at something is _____ (stare).

H. Challenge Words Write the Challenge Word that completes each sentence.

arbitrary	cartridge	sardines	inherited	parasites

1. Place the film in the _____ when the roll is done.

2. The heirs have _____ an old house.

3. The small fish are called _____ .

4. The fleas feeding on your dog are _____ .

5. My decision is based on good reasons and is not _____ .

I. Spelling and Writing Use as many of the Spelling Words, Other Word Forms, and Challenge Words as you can in sentences about one of the following titles. Then circle the spelling words you used. Proofread your spelling.

<u>Walking in the Rain</u> or <u>Stolen Goods</u>

Example: *Walking* (carefully) *in the rain is my* (favorite) *thing to do.*

20

A. Pretest Write each spelling word.

B. Spelling Words and Phrases

1.	wealth	lost their <u>wealth</u>
2.	healthy	<u>healthy</u> sea air
3.	spread	was <u>spread</u> on bread
4.	pleasant	was rarely <u>pleasant</u>
5.	steady	a <u>steady</u> motion
6.	instead	went out <u>instead</u>
7.	debt	not deeply in <u>debt</u>
8.	depth	unknown <u>depth</u>
9.	length	<u>length</u> and width
10.	strength	<u>strength</u> of an ox
11.	stretch	to bend and <u>stretch</u>
12.	wrench	to open with a <u>wrench</u>
13.	percent	twenty <u>percent</u>
14.	pledge	will <u>pledge</u> ten dollars
15.	effort	worth the <u>effort</u>
16.	error	corrected my <u>error</u>
17.	empire	ancient <u>empire</u>
18.	extra	<u>extra</u> effort
19.	expert	<u>expert</u> advice
20.	expensive	an <u>expensive</u> watch

Other Word Forms

wealthy, wealthier, wealthiest	wrenches, wrenched,
health, healthier, healthiest	wrenching
spreading	percents, percentage
pleasantly	pledges, pledging
steadies, steadier, steadiest	effortless, effortlessly
debts, debtor	errors
depths	empires
lengths, lengthy	extras
strengths, strengthen,	experts, expertly
strengthened	expense
stretches, stretched	

C. Visual Warm-up Write each word in its correct shape.

a.

b.

c.

d.

e.

f.

g.

h.

i.

j.

k.

l.

m.

n.

o.

p.

q.

r.

s.

t.

D. Let's Check E's All the words in the spelling list have a short *e* sound. In alphabetical order, write the spelling words where they belong.

Short *e* Spelled *e*

1. _____
2. _____
3. _____
4. _____
5. _____
6. _____
7. _____
8. _____
9. _____
10. _____
11. _____
12. _____
13. _____
14. _____

Short *e* Spelled *ea*

15. _____
16. _____
17. _____
18. _____
19. _____
20. _____

E. Scrambled Words Unscramble the underlined words so you can read the signs. Write the unscrambled words.

1. The repimE Supermarket
   1. _____

2. Save up to 40 prentce.
   2. _____

3. Stay thyhale. Use Garble Mouthwash.
   3. _____

4. You can chetstr your food dollar.
   4. _____

5. For that seaplant feeling, use Smeller's Soap!
   5. _____

6. Buy terax food at bargain prices.
   6. _____

7. Avoid the cheaper adespr. Use Butler's Creamy Butter.
   7. _____

8. Buy value nidaest of high costs.
   8. _____

9. Quality and savings is our dgeple.
   9. _____

10. Visit our produce ertpex.
    10. _____

11. We make every rtoffe to serve you well.
    11. _____

12. Special bargains for all our daesty customers.
    12. _____

13. Empire Supermarket only looks spenviexe.
    13. _____

14. Our new computer check-out stations are rerro free.
    14. _____

Spelling Words

wealth	healthy	spread	pleasant	steady
instead	debt	depth	length	strength
stretch	wrench	percent	pledge	effort
error	empire	extra	expert	expensive

F. Likes and Opposites

Write a spelling word for each meaning. Check your answers in the **Spelling Dictionary**.

1. a tool for turning nuts and bolts _____

2. to cover with a thin layer _____

3. additional _____

4. a strong try _____

5. a mistake _____

6. something owed _____

7. a person who has great knowledge on a subject _____

8. to promise _____

9. the parts in each hundred _____

10. as a substitute _____

11. a group of states or nations under one ruler _____

12. the distance from top to bottom _____

Write a spelling word for its opposite, or antonym.

13. sickly _____

14. width _____

15. shrink _____

16. shaking _____

17. weakness _____

18. cheap _____

19. disagreeable _____

20. poorness _____

G. Using Other Word Forms Write the Other Word Form (p. 80) that completes each series.

1. healthy, _____ , healthiest

2. wealthy, wealthier, _____

3. steady, steadier, _____

4. pledges, pledged, _____

5. stretches, _____ , stretching

H. Challenge Words Write the Challenge Word that completes each question.

penguins	effects	elevation	intently	membrane

1. Where is the cell's _____ located?

2. Why are you studying that picture so _____ ?

3. At what _____ does the plane normally fly?

4. Don't the _____ look as if they're wearing tuxedos?

5. Do you feel the _____ of working too much?

I. Spelling and Writing Use as many of the Spelling Words, Other Word Forms, and Challenge Words as you can to write imaginary newspaper headlines. Then circle the spelling words you used. Proofread your spelling.

Example: *Added* (*Strength*) *! New* (*Wrench*) *Makes Work* (*Effortless*)

21

A. Pretest Write each spelling word.

B. Spelling Words and Phrases

1. sting — to <u>sting</u> like a bee
2. stitch — to <u>stitch</u> the rip
3. switch — light <u>switch</u>
4. swiftly — flew away <u>swiftly</u>
5. whisper — a <u>whisper</u> in the dark
6. whistle — a piercing <u>whistle</u>
7. disturb — will <u>disturb</u> the silence
8. acid — an <u>acid</u> taste
9. timid — a <u>timid</u> child
10. rapid — <u>rapid</u> transit
11. stupid — felt very <u>stupid</u>
12. liquid — melted into <u>liquid</u>
13. splendid — <u>splendid</u> sunset
14. forbidden — a <u>forbidden</u> place
15. taxis — <u>taxis</u> for hire
16. campus — college <u>campus</u>
17. wander — to <u>wander</u> and wonder
18. landscape — an icy <u>landscape</u>
19. handkerchief — red <u>handkerchief</u>
20. paragraph — final <u>paragraph</u>

Other Word Forms

stinging, stung
stitches, stitched, stitching
switches, switching
swift, swiftest
whispers, whispering
whistled, whistling
disturbing, disturbance
acids, acidic
timidly
rapids, rapidly
stupidly, stupidity
liquids
splendidly
forbid, forbade, forbidding
taxi
campuses
wandered, wanderer
landscapes
handkerchiefs
paragraphs

C. Visual Warm-up Write each word in its correct shape.

a.
b.
c.
d.
e.
f.
g.
h.
i.
j.
k.
l.
m.
n.
o.
p.
q.
r.
s.
t.

D. Riddles

Answer these questions by writing an <u>id</u> word from the spelling list.

1. What <u>id</u> is not allowed? _____

2. What <u>id</u> is shy? _____

3. What <u>id</u> is wonderful? _____

4. What <u>id</u> burns? _____

5. What <u>id</u> spills? _____

6. What <u>id</u> is not smart? _____

7. What <u>id</u> is fast? _____

Answer these questions by writing an <u>itch</u> word.

8. What <u>itch</u> is sewn? _____

9. What <u>itch</u> changes? _____

Answer this question by writing an <u>if</u> word.

10. What <u>if</u> moves quickly? _____

Answer these questions by writing an <u>is</u> word.

11. What <u>is</u> annoys? _____

12. What <u>is</u> calls a dog? _____

13. What <u>is</u> speaks quietly? _____

14. Sometimes *i* sounds like long *e*. What word does this describe? _____

15. Use the six remaining words and as many Other Word Forms (p. 84) as you can to make a crossword or a word hunt puzzle in the grid.

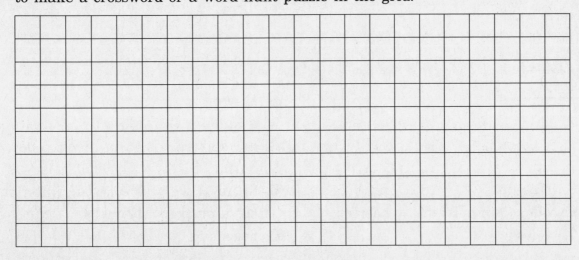

Spelling Words

sting	stitch	switch	swiftly	whisper
whistle	disturb	acid	timid	rapid
stupid	liquid	splendid	forbidden	taxis
campus	wander	landscape	handkerchief	paragraph

E. Crossword Puzzle Solve the puzzle by using all the words from the spelling list. Write the words. Check your answers in the **Spelling Dictionary**.

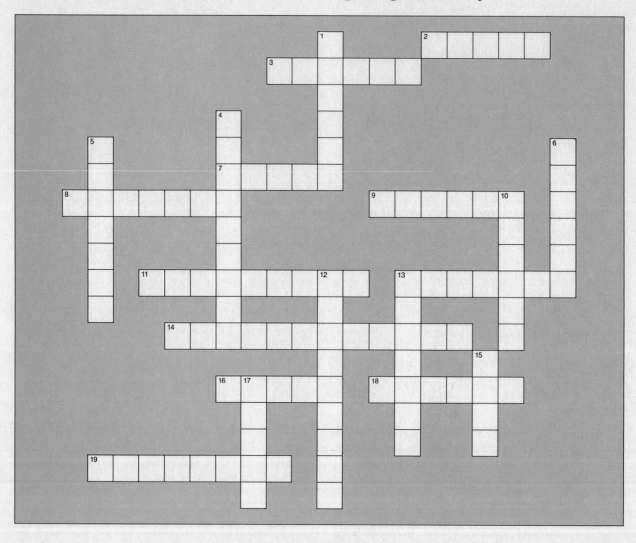

Across

2. shy
3. to exchange
7. fast
8. to bother
9. college grounds
11. scenery
13. soft speech
14. a small cloth
16. a bee's revenge
18. to sew
19. wonderful

Down

1. a fluid
4. not allowed
5. quickly
6. to travel without a purpose
10. not smart
12. a division of a story
13. a high-pitched, shrill noise
15. a sour, bitter taste
17. cabs

F. Using Other Word Forms Write the Other Word Form (p. 84) that completes each sentence.

1. A person who did something foolishly did it _____ (stupid).

2. A person who speaks softly is _____ (whisper).

3. A person who is bothering others can be very _____ (disturb).

4. A person who runs quickly runs _____ (rapid).

5. A person who roams aimlessly is a _____ (wander).

G. Challenge Words Write the Challenge Word that completes each sentence.

abstract	actual	thrifty	eliminate	registered

1. I know the _____ number of children in each classroom.

2. A _____ person will always save money.

3. The company must _____ ten jobs.

4. Twenty guests _____ during the afternoon.

5. I have trouble understanding _____ concepts.

H. Spelling and Writing Use as many of the Spelling Words, Other Word Forms, and Challenge Words as you can to write a letter to someone you know. Tell about an adventure you had recently. Then circle the spelling words you used. Proofread your spelling.

Example: *I left the (taxi) and (wandered) around the (campus) .*

22

A. Pretest Write each spelling word.

B. Spelling Words and Phrases

1. loss — profit and <u>loss</u>
2. polish — silver <u>polish</u>
3. volume — great <u>volume</u> of water
4. rotten — a <u>rotten</u> banana
5. project — assigned a <u>project</u>
6. properly — <u>properly</u> dressed
7. gossip — shared some <u>gossip</u>
8. common — <u>common</u> cold
9. comment — to <u>comment</u> on it
10. companion — a loyal <u>companion</u>
11. concert — jazz <u>concert</u>
12. contemplate — will <u>contemplate</u> the puzzle
13. solving — <u>solving</u> the mystery
14. resolve — will <u>resolve</u> the problem
15. response — a friendly <u>response</u>
16. adopt — will <u>adopt</u> the child
17. forehead — sunburned <u>forehead</u>
18. fortune — empty <u>fortune</u> cookie
19. borrowed — <u>borrowed</u> a sweater
20. tailor — made by a <u>tailor</u>

Other Word Forms

losses	concerts
polishes, polished, polishing	contemplates, contemplating
volumes	solve, solved
rot, rottenest	resolved, resolving
projects	responses, responsible
proper	adopts, adopted, adoption
gossips, gossiping	foreheads
commonly	fortunes, fortunately
commented	borrrow, borrowing
companions, companionship	tailors, tailoring

C. Visual Warm-up Write each word in its correct shape.

a.
b.
c.
d.
e.
f.
g.
h.
i.
j.
k.
l.
m.
n.
o.
p.
q.
r.
s.
t.

D. Sort Your *O*'s Write each spelling word where it belongs. A word may go in more than one list.

Letter *o* in the First or Only Syllable

1. _____   9. _____
2. _____   10. _____
3. _____   11. _____
4. _____   12. _____
5. _____   13. _____
6. _____   14. _____
7. _____   15. _____
8. _____   16. _____

Letter *o* in the Second Syllable

17. _____
18. _____
19. _____
20. _____
21. _____
22. _____

Letter *o* in the Third Syllable

23. _____

E. Bases and Suffixes The spelling list contains sixteen base words and four words with suffixes. Write each spelling word.

Words with Suffixes	Base Words		Words with Suffixes	Base Words
1. losses	_____		11. resolved	_____
2. concerts	_____		12. commonly	_____
3. projects	_____		13. contemplates	_____
4. gossiping	_____		14. commented	_____
5. polishing	_____		15. volumes	_____
6. fortunes	_____		16. responses	_____
7. foreheads	_____		17. _____	solve
8. tailoring	_____		18. _____	rot
9. companions	_____		19. _____	borrow
10. adoption	_____		20. _____	proper

Spelling Words

loss	polish	volume	rotten	project
properly	gossip	common	comment	companion
concert	contemplate	solving	resolve	response
adopt	forehead	fortune	borrowed	tailor

F. Synonym Match-ups Write a spelling word for each synonym.

1. explain _____

2. answer _____

3. remark _____

4. accept _____

5. brow _____

6. rumor _____

7. wealth _____

8. used _____

9. friend _____

10. performance _____

11. decoding _____

12. think _____

13. decayed _____

14. correctly _____

15. ordinary _____

16. shine _____

17. seamstress _____

18. loudness _____

19. assignment _____

20. decrease _____

G. Using Other Word Forms Write the Other Word Form (p. 88) that completes each sentence.

1. They were shining the car. They were _____ (polish) it with wax.

2. The family found a stray cat. They _____ (adopt) it as their own.

3. The announcer praised the tennis player's ability. He _____ (comment) on it.

4. I'm lending money to my brother. He is _____ (borrowed) it.

5. That man caused the accident. He is _____ (response) for it.

H. Challenge Words Write the Challenge Word that completes each sentence.

possibly	abolished	glossary	goggles	orchids

1. A student might use a _____ to find a meaning of a word.

2. A ski racer needs _____ to protect her eyes.

3. A florist might sell _____ .

4. A protester might insist that an unfair law be _____ .

5. The animal trainer _____ works with elephants.

I. Spelling and Writing Write the following phrases in sentences. Proofread your spelling.

Example: *He responded with a good comment.*

1. a good <u>comment</u>
2. trusted <u>companion</u>
3. <u>properly</u> straightened
4. the fourth <u>volume</u>
5. will <u>polish</u> the ring
6. wrinkled <u>forehead</u>
7. <u>loss</u> of power
8. <u>rotten</u> garbage
9. to <u>adopt</u> an animal
10. outdoor <u>concert</u>

11. <u>solving</u> the puzzle
12. a great <u>fortune</u>
13. <u>common</u> practice
14. to <u>resolve</u> the problem
15. dangerous <u>gossip</u>
16. sewn by a <u>tailor</u>
17. science <u>project</u>
18. correct <u>response</u>
19. to <u>contemplate</u> the matter
20. <u>borrowed</u> a pencil

23

A. Pretest Write each spelling word.

B. Spelling Words and Phrases

1.	bluff	called their bluff
2.	cunning	known for its cunning
3.	rudder	the boat's rudder
4.	suffer	to suffer from a fall
5.	succeed	if you can succeed
6.	suddenly	suddenly fell
7.	suggest	whatever you suggest
8.	supply	a supply of fresh fruit
9.	support	to support the wall
10.	struggle	a struggle to breathe
11.	subject	subject of a sentence
12.	suspect	to doubt and suspect
13.	punctual	always punctual
14.	punish	no need to punish
15.	publish	will publish your story
16.	vulgar	a vulgar sight
17.	adjust	to adjust the brakes
18.	unjust	an unjust decision
19.	result	waited for the result
20.	discuss	should discuss further

Other Word Forms

bluffs, bluffing
cunningly
rudders
suffered, suffering
succeeded, succeeding,
  successful
sudden
suggests, suggestion
supplies, supplied,
  supplying
supported, supportive
struggled, struggling

subjected, subjecting
suspected, suspecting
punctually
punishes, punished,
  punishment
publishes, publishing
vulgarly
adjusted
just, unjustly
resulted, resulting
discusses, discussion

C. Visual Warm-up Write each word in its correct shape.

a.
b.
c.
d.
e.
f.
g.
h.
i.
j.
k.
l.
m.
n.
o.
p.
q.
r.
s.
t.

D. Word Search The spelling words can be found in the word puzzle. The words appear across and down. Circle and write the words.

Across

1. _____

2. _____

3. _____

4. _____

5. _____

6. _____

7. _____

8. _____

```
s u s p e c t d s u b j e c t
u n u a s u e i u r l s x c r
d j g z u n r s p u u t e n e
d u g w p n p c p d f r p a s
e s e i p i l u o d f u s d u
n t s r l n e s r e m g h j l
l p t n y g r s t r e g d u t
y q p u n i s h p u b l i s h
v u l g a r s r m a q e e t a
p u n c t u a l t p o r s m r
s u f f e r e s u c c e e d o
```

Down

9. _____

10. _____

11. _____

12. _____

13. _____

14. _____

15. _____

16. _____

17. _____

18. _____

19. _____

20. _____

E. Double Your Trouble Write the spelling words that fit the patterns below. Each word has a double consonant.

1. blu __ __ _____

2. su __ __ er _____

3. su __ __ enly _____

4. ru __ __ er _____

5. su __ __ eed _____

6. su __ __ est _____

7. su __ __ ly _____

8. cu __ __ ing _____

9. su __ __ ort _____

10. stru __ __ le _____

F. Generally Speaking Write a spelling word for the group it best fits.

1. change, fix, _____

2. topic, title, _____

3. ending, conclusion, _____

4. unfair, dishonest, _____

5. crude, coarse, _____

6. doubt, question, _____

7. discipline, restrict, _____

8. write, print, _____

Spelling Words

bluff	*cunning*	*rudder*	*suffer*	*succeed*
suddenly	*suggest*	*supply*	*support*	*struggle*
subject	*suspect*	*punctual*	*punish*	*publish*
vulgar	*adjust*	*unjust*	*result*	*discuss*

G. Be a Sentence Detective Unscramble the word under each blank. Write each unscrambled word.

1. If the _____ of your story will interest many people, the

bujects

   newspaper will _____ it.

bupshli

2. The acrobat will _____ his feet to _____ his partner.

staduj — posrtpu

3. I will _____ you with a ladder so you don't have to

plyusp

   _____ to wash the windows.

guelgstr

4. The newscasters will _____ the _____ of the election.

csdsisu — ltuser

5. The judge does _____ the known criminal, but for lack of

spectus

   evidence she will not _____ him.

shunip

6. I strongly _____ that you stay away from that

steggus

   _____ fox.

ngnunci

7. I will _____ from embarrassment if I am accused of

ruseff

   _____ behavior.

guavrl

8. A huge wave _____ smashed against the small boat and tore

lddensyu

   away its _____ .

rudedr

9. The cardplayer's clever _____ will probably _____ .

fublf — cuecdse

10. The children complained about the _____ punishment for not

junstu

    being _____ .

nctluuap

H. Using Other Word Forms Write the Other Word Form (p. 92) that completes each series.

1. punishes, _____ , punishing

2. suspects, suspected, _____

3. stuggles, struggled, _____

4. supports, _____ , supporting

5. results, _____ , resulting

I. Challenge Words Write the Challenge Word that completes each phrase.

customary	punishment	success	puppets	sustained

1. marionettes or _____

2. usual or _____

3. prolonged or _____

4. victory or _____

5. discipline or _____

J. Spelling and Writing Write in your journal. Use as many of the Spelling Words, Other Word Forms, and Challenge Words as you can to write a page about catching a big fish. Then circle the spelling words you used. Remember when writing a journal to include the date, the time, and what happened. Proofread your spelling.

Example: *June 12–2:00—The two (struggling) fish (suddenly) looked like puppets on strings.*

24

~~acid~~	~~effort~~	~~instead~~	~~spare~~	suddenly
~~bluff~~	~~extra~~	properly	~~splendid~~	~~taxis~~
~~common~~	~~farewell~~	punctual	~~strength~~	~~timid~~
~~contemplate~~	~~favorable~~	~~rotten~~	stupid	~~various~~
~~debt~~	~~fortune~~	~~scarcely~~	~~succeed~~	~~vulgar~~

A. Word Search Twenty-four Other Word Forms and one spelling word can be found in the word puzzle. The words appear across, down, and diagonally. Circle and write each word. If you need help, use the **Spelling Dictionary**.

REVIEW

Across

1. punctually
2. scarcest
3. bluffing
4. instead
5. efforts
6. splendidly
7. ACids
8. timidly
9. fAvors
10. debts
11. extras
12. farewells
13. contemplates
14. succeeded

```
p u n c t u a l l y u p v i
f r s c a r c e s t w l u n
o m o b l u f f i n g s l s
r t n p i n s t e a d t g t
t o a u e b j x u t r u a r
u e f f o r t s b j k p r e
n s p l e n d i d l y i l n
a g s n a c i d s z c d y g
t b d p g h o n v a r l v t
e c m l a t i m i d l y a h
l f a v o r s y m k h r r e
y d e b t s e u n o r o i n
e x t r a s c d d g n t e t
f a r e w e l l s d s l t a
c o n t e m p l a t e s y x
s u c c e e d e d u v n w i
```

Down

15. fortunately
16. stupidly
17. rot
18. vulgarly
19. variety
20. strengthen
21. tAxi

Diagonally

22. proper
23. Commonly
24. sudden
25. spared

starve	charity	department	stare	carefully
wealth	spread	percent	error	healthy
whistle	forbidden	liquid	sting	switch
loss	solving	companion	project	struggle
result	unjust	suffer	discuss	response

B. Quotable Quotes Write Other Word Forms to replace the spelling words printed under the blanks. If you need help, use the **Spelling Dictionary.**

1. "Be ___careful___ not to be ___stung___," the beekeeper droned.
    (carefully) (sting)

2. "All of Alice's ___responses___ will be ignored when the ___discussion___
    (response) (discuss)
    is over," the hatter chattered madly.

3. "Humpty Dumpty's ___errors___ have ___resulted___ in a
    (error) (result)
    shattering experience," the king's man cracked openly.

4. "The basketball team has ___suffered___ unfortunate ___losses___
    (suffer) (loss)
    this season," the coach charged defensively.

5. "Only royal ___projects___ are planned to benefit Snow White's
    (project)
    ___charity___," the prince contributed charmingly.
    (charity)

6. "Drinking plenty of ___liquids___ will improve your ___health___,"
    (liquid) (healthy)
    the doctor prescribed patiently.

7. "I've been ___struggling___ for half an hour ___spreading___ this ginger
    (struggle) (spread)
    mixture," the cookie baker snapped crisply.

8. "Some ___wealthy___ emperors treat people ___unjustly___ while
    (wealth) (unjust)
    others have the golden touch," King Midas reflected radiantly.

9. "___Solving___ these ___percentage___ problems," the math teacher added.
    (solving) (percent)

10. "Eight reindeer ___companions___ and I visited hundreds of toy
    (companion)
    ___departments___ during December," Santa caroled merrily.
    (department)

11. "I ___forbide___ loud ___whistles___," the coach blasted.
    (forbidden) (whistle)

12. "After ___staring___ at steaks and chops all day, I was
    (stare)
    ___starving___ for a hamburger," the broiler cook beefed.
    (starve)

13. "___Switching___ your toothpaste could improve your teeth," the dentist drilled.
    (switch)

REVIEW

armor	declare	regard	sheriff	article
stretch	pledge	expert	empire	length
whisper	landscape	stitch	disturb	wander
volume	resolve	adopt	comment	gossip
adjust	suspect	subject	suggest	publish

C. Word Operations Use words from the spelling list to complete the exercises. If you need help, use the **Spelling Dictionary**.

Operation Past Tense Write the *ed* form of each word.

1. declare _declared_
2. adjust _adjusted_
3. armor _armored_
4. adopt _adopted_
5. disturb _disturbed_
6. wander _wandered_
7. regard _regarded_
8. stretch _stretched_

9. pledge _pledged_
10. whisper _whispered_
11. resolve _resolved_
12. stitch _stitched_
13. gossip _gossiped_
14. comment _commented_
15. publish _published_
16. suggest _suggested_

Operation Plural Write the *s* form of each word.

17. landscape _landscapes_
18. subject _subjects_
19. sheriff _sheriffs_
20. length _lengths_
21. expert _experts_

22. empire _empires_
23. suspect _suspects_
24. article _articles_
25. volume _volumes_

Operation Noun Write the *ion* or *ation* form of each word. Some words need a change before the suffix is added.

26. declare _declaration_
27. suggest _suggestion_
28. adopt _adoption_

29. suspect _suspension_ _suspection_
30. publish _publication_
31. resolve _resolution_

■ ~~warehouse~~	★ ~~garbage~~	▲ ~~argument~~	◆ ~~charming~~	● ~~prepare~~
depth	~~wrench~~	steady	~~expensive~~	pleasant
rapid	~~swiftly~~	handkerchief	campus	paragraph
forehead	~~tailor~~	concert	polish	~~borrowed~~
~~support~~	~~cunning~~	~~supply~~	punish	~~rudder~~

D. Books and Authors

Decide which Other Word Forms or spelling words will complete the book titles. Write each word and capitalize it. Use each word or its Other Word Form only once. Use the **Spelling Dictionary**.

1. Beauty and ◆ _Charm_ by Izzy Cute

2. Rowing ■ _Rapid_ Down the Stream by Whyte Waters

3. Some Rock 'n' Roll ▲ _Concert_ by Lowd E. Nuff

4. Reducing Personal ◆ _Expenses_ by Nita Budgett

5. Eliminating Litter and ★ _Garbage_ by Phil D. Dumpster

6. The ★ _Cunning_ Foxes by Barry Sligh

7. Backbones and ■ _Foreheads_ by Ann Atomy

8. Dealing ● _Pleasantly_ with Others by Willy Smyle Moore

9. The Case of the ◆ _Polished_ Apple by T. Churz Pett

10. No More Scolding or ◆ _Punishment_ by Lett Up

11. Crying Eyes and Dry ▲ _Hankerchief_ by Will I. Sobb

12. Cramped Spaces and Filled ■ _Warehouses_ by Alotta Stock

13. The Student's Guide Book to College ◆ _Campus_ by A. Dean

14. New ● _Rudders_ for Old Sailing Ships by Nina N. Pinter

15. Sometimes ▲ _Argue_ ; Sometimes Agree by R. B. Trator

16. Screwdrivers and ★ _Wrenches_ for Every Occasion by Tern N. Twist

17. Writing Better ● _Paragraph_ by Letz Wright

18. Safer and ▲ _Steadier_ Ladders by U. May Clime

19. More a Lender, Less a ● _Borrower_ by Yul B. Richer

20. From the ■ _Depth_ of the Oceans by C. Waters

21. Camping Needs and ▲ _Supplies_ by Mark A. Trail

22. Be Alert; Be ● _Prepared_ by I. M. Reddy

23. Seamstresses and ★ _Tailors_ Through the Ages by Pinz N. Needles

24. Aiding and ■ _Support_ the Dock Worker by Steve A. Dore

25. Today's Sleekest and ★ _Swiftest_ Runners by Mara Thonn

REVIEW

25

A. Pretest Write each spelling word.

B. Spelling Words and Phrases

1. joint — hinge of the joint
2. boiler — steam from the boiler
3. spoil — if the milk will spoil
4. avoid — tried to avoid
5. loyal — loyal to friends
6. voyage — another voyage
7. destroy — accidentally destroy
8. weight — too much weight
9. freight — loaded with freight
10. neighboring — neighboring countries
11. active — an active life
12. action — filled with action
13. athlete — a skillful athlete
14. accent — a southwestern accent
15. patent — should patent your invention
16. pattern — traced the pattern
17. lantern — a flickering lantern
18. salad — soup and salad
19. channel — crossed the channel
20. rapidly — rapidly drained out

Other Word Forms

joints	actively, activity, actions
boil, boiled, boiling	
spoiled, spoiling	athletes, athletic
avoids, avoided, avoiding	accents, accenting
loyally, loyalty	patents, patented, patenting
voyaging, voyager	
destroyed, destroying destruction	patterns, patterned
	lanterns
weights, weighing	salads
freighter	channels, channeled
neighbor, neighbors	rapid

a.
b.
c.
d.
e.
f.
g.
h.
i.
j.
k.
l.
m.
n.
o.
p.
q.
r.
s.
t.

D. Word Search The spelling words can be found in the word puzzle. The words appear across and down. Circle and write the words.

Across

1. _____

2. _____

3. _____

4. _____

5. _____

6. _____

7. _____

8. _____

9. _____

10. _____

11. _____

Down

12. _____

13. _____

```
x  y  z  f  p  a  t  e  n  t  j  h  y  c
o  l  b  r  c  g  p  e  a  v  o  i  d  h
d  a  w  e  a  c  c  e  n  t  i  b  a  a
p  n  e  i  g  h  b  o  r  i  n  g  c  n
a  t  i  g  s  p  o  i  l  k  t  l  t  n
t  e  g  h  s  s  i  v  t  j  x  w  i  e
t  r  h  t  a  p  l  o  y  a  l  n  v  l
e  n  t  e  l  i  e  u  a  y  z  m  e  k
r  f  b  h  a  l  r  a  p  i  d  l  y  n
n  i  d  c  d  a  c  t  i  o  n  m  o  l
g  a  t  h  l  e  t  e  v  o  y  a  g  e
j  d  e  s  t  r  o  y  p  t  o  r  q  u
```

14. _____

15. _____

16. _____

17. _____

18. _____

19. _____

20. _____

E. Word Match-ups Write a spelling word that best fits each phrase or word below.

1. goods _____

2. travel _____

3. dodge _____

4. to wreck _____

5. quickly _____

6. lamp _____

7. next to _____

8. busy _____

9. faithful _____

10. rot _____

11. model used for tracing _____

12. one who plays sports _____

13. mixture of vegetables _____

14. knee or elbow _____

15. a hot-water storage tank _____

16. heaviness _____

17. sole rights for invention _____

18. TV station _____

19. local speech pattern _____

20. movement _____

Spelling Words

joint	boiler	spoil	avoid	loyal
voyage	destroy	weight	freight	neighboring
active	action	athlete	accent	patent
pattern	lantern	salad	channel	rapidly

F. Finding Words The words in the spelling list appear in the beginning (A-H), middle (I-Q), or end (R-Z) of the **Spelling Dictionary**. Write each word.

Beginning A-H

1. _____
2. _____
3. _____
4. _____
5. _____
6. _____
7. _____
8. _____
9. _____

Middle I-Q

10. _____
11. _____
12. _____
13. _____
14. _____
15. _____

End R-Z

16. _____
17. _____
18. _____
19. _____
20. _____

G. The Treasure Map Unscramble the scrambled words to form words from the spelling list. Write the words.

1. teparnt _ _ _ □ _ _ _ _
2. eghtifr _ _ _ _ _ □ _ _
3. cantec _ _ _ □ _ _ _
4. trnanel _ _ _ _ _ □ _
5. strodey _ _ _ _ _ □ _
6. laloy _ _ □ _ _
7. intoca □ _ _ _ _ _

8. dlsaa _ _ □ _ _
9. intjo □ _ _ _ _
10. agyvoe _ _ _ _ _ □
11. ewight □ _ _ _ _ _
12. thelate _ _ _ _ □ _ _
13. lennach _ _ _ _ _ _ □
14. spoli □ _ _ _ _

15. Write the boxed letter in each spelling word in order (1–14), and find out what

is in the treasure chest: _ _ _   _ _ _ _ _ _ _   _ _ _ _ _ _ _ _ .

H. Using Other Word Forms Write the Other Word Forms (p. 100) that complete the paragraph.

One hundred **(1.)** _athletes_ (athlete) boarded

a **(2.)** _freighter_ (freight) in early spring. They were

(3.) _voyaging_ (voyage) to an island for training. They

were **(4.)** _avoiding_ (avoid) photographers at the dock so

their surprise trip would not be **(5.)** _destroyed_ (destroy).

I. Challenge Words Write the Challenge Word that completes each question.

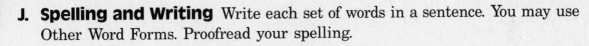

| celebration | crusaders | embroidered | enjoyment | disappointed |

1. Who _embroidered_ the stitches on the tablecloth?

2. Were you _disappointed_ at the loss of the tennis match?

3. When will the Labor Day _celebration_ begin?

4. Are they _crusaders_ for a clean environment?

5. Did the new puppy bring _enjoyment_ to the sick child?

J. Spelling and Writing Write each set of words in a sentence. You may use Other Word Forms. Proofread your spelling.

> Example: action–patent–pattern *I needed quick action to get*
> *a patent for my pattern.*

1. salad–weight–avoid

2. boiler–destroy–active

3. athlete–rapidly–joint

4. channel–neighboring–voyage

5. freight–lantern–spoil

6. loyal–accent

26

A. Pretest Write each spelling word.

B. Spelling Words and Phrases

1. metal — new metal detector
2. method — standard method
3. gentle — in a gentle way
4. velvet — a velvet cushion
5. lettuce — head of lettuce
6. seldom — seldom smiled
7. selfish — a selfish reason
8. special — for a special day
9. whether — whether to go
10. accept — to accept first prize
11. affect — will affect your plans
12. collect — to collect a pailful
13. expect — can expect a crowd
14. respect — a sign of respect
15. neglect — care or neglect
16. object — if they object
17. insects — as insects fly by
18. directed — used as directed
19. defense — the country's defense
20. expense — much greater expense

Other Word Forms

metals, metallic	expected, expecting
methods	respected, respectable
gently, gentler, gentlest	neglected, neglectful
velvety	objected, objecting,
seldomly	objection
selfishly	insect
specials, specialize,	direct, directing,
specialty	direction
accepts, accepting	defend, defending,
affected, affecting	defender, defensive
collected, collecting,	expensive
collection	

C. Visual Warm-up Write each word in its correct shape.

a.
b.
c.
d.
e.
f.
g.
h.
i.
j.
k.
l.
m.
n.
o.
p.
q.
r.
s.
t.

D. Word Riddles Answer each question by writing an <u>ect</u>, <u>ense</u>, <u>sel</u>, or <u>met</u> word from the spelling list.

1. What <u>ect</u> do you give to elders? _____

2. What <u>ect</u> makes you sad? _____

3. What <u>ect</u> influences or changes? _____

4. What <u>ect</u> opposes something? _____

5. What <u>ect</u> can bug you? _____

6. What <u>ect</u> might you do with stamps? _____

7. What <u>ect</u> do you await? _____

8. What <u>ect</u> did the band leader do? _____

9. What <u>ense</u> is provided by a fort? _____

10. What <u>ense</u> stops you from buying? _____

11. What <u>sel</u> tells how often Valentine's Day comes? _____

12. What <u>sel</u> describes a stingy person? _____

13. What <u>met</u> shines when polished? _____

14. What <u>met</u> is a way of doing something? _____

15. Write the six remaining spelling words in alphabetical order.

   a. _____   d. _____

   b. _____   e. _____

   c. _____   f. _____

Spelling Words

metal	method	gentle	velvet	lettuce	seldom
selfish	special	whether	accept	affect	collect
expect	respect	neglect	object	insects	directed
defense	expense				

E. Word Search The spelling words can be found in the word puzzle. The words appear across, down, and diagonally. Circle and write the words.

Across

1. _____

2. _____

3. _____

4. _____

5. _____

6. _____

Down

7. _____

8. _____

9. _____

10. _____

11. _____

12. _____

13. _____

14. _____

```
v e l v e t w r o l
s e l f i s h n m e
g e n t l e e d e t
c o l l e c t e c t
r e m d o s h f t u
e m x e o r e e u c
s n e p t m r n r e
p e x t e h n s e i
e g p s a c o e o n
c l e p a l t d b s
t e n e f l o l j e
t c s c f l i w e c
o t e i e e r n c t
l m e a c c e p t s
f e u l t r o e t r
i d i r e c t e d e
```

Diagonally

15. _____

16. _____

17. _____

18. _____

19. _____

20. _____

F. Homographs Use the **Spelling Dictionary** to check the meanings of the homographs below. Then write each homograph in a separate sentence.

1. ob ject′ _____

2. ob′ ject _____

G. Using Other Word Forms Write the Other Word Form (p. 104) that is the opposite of each word or phrase.

1. offensive _defensive_ (defense)
2. agreed with _objected_ (object)
3. cheap _expensive_ (expense)
4. paid attention to _neglected_ (neglect)
5. got rid of _collected_ (collect)

H. Challenge Words Write the Challenge Word that completes each sentence.

aggressive	electrical	shepherd	infection	rendered

1. When the lambs wander, the _shepherd_ searches for them.
2. When a blackout occurs, _electrical_ appliances are useless.
3. When an injury is not treated, _infection_ can occur.
4. When people argue and fight, their behavior is _aggressive_.
5. When the alarm was sounded, the fire department _rendered_ assistance.

I. Spelling and Writing Use as many of the Spelling Words, Other Word Forms, and Challenge Words as you can in sentences about one of the following titles. Then circle the spelling words you used. Proofread your spelling.

Through the Frightening Jungle or Yesterday's Homework

Example: *They (neglected) to (collect) the (gentle) moth.*

27

A. Pretest Write each spelling word.

B. Spelling Words and Phrases

1.	abandon	had to abandon ship
2.	advantage	took advantage of
3.	advertise	will advertise on TV
4.	accident	to witness the accident
5.	attractive	an attractive family
6.	battery	a flashlight battery
7.	passage	had read a short passage
8.	traffic	as traffic thinned
9.	happiness	shared our happiness
10.	cabinet	from the cabinet
11.	capital	a capital letter
12.	catalog	1400-page catalog
13.	chapter	the last chapter
14.	vanity	pride and vanity
15.	practical	a practical set of tools
16.	factories	shoe factories
17.	exactly	exactly on time
18.	example	a good example
19.	traveler	a tired traveler
20.	material	stronger material

Other Word Forms

abandons, abandoned, abandoning
advantages
advertises, advertised, advertising, advertisement
accidents, accidentally, attract, attractively
batteries
passages, passenger
happy, happiest
cabinets
capitals
catalogs
chapters
vain, vanities
practice, practically
factory
exact, exactness
examples
travel, traveled, traveling, travelers
materials, materialize

C. Visual Warm-up Write each word in its correct shape.

a.
b.
c.
d.
e.
f.
g.
h.
i.
j.
k.
l.
m.
n.
o.
p.
q.
r.
s.
t.

D. Generally Speaking Write each spelling word for the group it best fits. Next to all but one spelling word, write an Other Word Form (p. 108).

Other Word Forms

1. accurately, carefully, _exactly_ _____

2. book division, several passages, _chapter_ _____

3. pretty, appealing, _attractive_ _____

4. main city, Washington, D.C., _capital_ _____

5. power, dry cell, _battery_ _____

6. order form, book, _catalog_ _____

7. pride, boastfulness, _vanity_ _____

8. sample, model, _example_ _____

9. cloth, fabric, _material_ _____

10. leave, desert, _abandon_ _____

11. crash, dent, _accident_ _____

12. joy, pleasure, _happiness_ _____

13. sensible, useful, _practical_ _____

14. cupboard, closet, _cabinet_ _____

15. head start, benefit, _advantage_ _____

16. sell, announce, _advertise_ _____

17. buildings, industries, _factories_ _____

18. tourist, hiker, _traveler_ _____

19. section, paragraph, _passage_ _____

20. vehicles, noise, _traffic_ _____

Spelling Words

abandon	advantage	advertise	accident	attractive
battery	passage	traffic	happiness	cabinet
capital	catalog	chapter	vanity	material
practical	factories	exactly	example	traveler

E. Base Words The spelling list contains thirteen base words and seven words that are not base words. Write each spelling word.

Words That Are Not Base Words	Base Words	Words That Are Not Base Words	Base Words
1. accidentally	_____	**11.** advantages	_____
2. advertisement	_____	**12.** passages	_____
3. capitals	_____	**13.** _____	happy
4. abandoning	_____	**14.** _____	vain
5. examples	_____	**15.** _____	practice
6. materials	_____	**16.** _____	factory
7. batteries	_____	**17.** _____	exact
8. cabinets	_____	**18.** _____	attract
9. catalogs	_____	**19.** _____	travel
10. chapters	_____		

20. Write the one base word not used above. _____

F. Using Other Word Forms Write the Other Word Form (p. 108) that replaces each underlined word or phrase.

1. The store <u>announced in the newspaper</u> an upcoming sale. *advertised* (advertise)

2. Don't forget to buy <u>power supplies</u> for the flashlight. *batteries* (battery)

3. She <u>left</u> her disabled car and walked the remaining five blocks. *abandoned* (abandon)

4. He was a <u>rider</u> on the morning train. *passagenger* (passage)

5. I dialed the wrong number <u>by mistake</u>. *accidently* (accident)

G. Challenge Words Write the Challenge Word that completes each analogy.

academic	calories	expanded	humanity	galaxies

1. **smaller** is to **larger** as **contracted** is to _*expanded*_

2. **sand grains** is to **beaches** as **stars** is to _*galaxies*_

3. **office** is to **clerical** as **classroom** is to _*academic*_

4. **electrical units** is to **watts** as **heat units** is to _*calories*_

5. **beet** is to **vegetable** as **man** is to _*humanity*_

H. Spelling and Writing Use as many of the Spelling Words, Other Word Forms, and Challenge Words as you can in sentences about one of the following titles. Then circle the spelling words you used. Proofread your spelling.

A Department Store or The Election

Example: *There is an* (attractive) *department store located in an old* (factory) *.*

28

A. Pretest Write each spelling word.

B. Spelling Words and Phrases

1.	limit	to limit their time
2.	spirit	played with spirit
3.	admit	to admit we're wrong
4.	credit	to their credit
5.	profit	will profit greatly
6.	exhibit	a crafts exhibit
7.	deposit	made a bank deposit
8.	permitted	no animals permitted
9.	permission	permission to leave
10.	twist	to twist out of shape
11.	assist	can assist me later
12.	insist	if you insist
13.	dentist	went to the dentist
14.	impulse	a sudden impulse
15.	inning	may win in the final inning
16.	income	earned a good income
17.	dismiss	to dismiss for recess
18.	district	school district
19.	slippers	tripped over slippers
20.	scissors	to cut with scissors

Other Word Forms

limited, limiting,
  limitation
spirited
admitted, admitting,
  admittance
credits, credited, crediting
profited, profiting
exhibited, exhibition
deposited, depositing
permit, permitting
twisted, twisting

assisted, assistant
insisted, insisting
dentists, dentistry
impulses
innings
incomes, incoming
dismisses, dismissing,
  dismissal
districts
slip, slipper, slippery

C. Visual Warm-up Write each word in its correct shape.

a.

b.

c.

d.

e.

f.

g.

h.

i.

j.

k.

l.

m.

n.

o.

p.

q.

r.

s.

t.

D. The *I*'s Have It All the spelling words have a short *i* sound. Write each spelling word where it belongs. A word may go in more than one list.

Words That End with *it*

1. _____
2. _____
3. _____
4. _____
5. _____
6. _____
7. _____

Words That End with *ist*

16. _____   18. _____
17. _____   19. _____

Words with a Short *i* Sound Followed by a Double Consonant

20. _____   23. _____
21. _____   24. _____
22. _____   25. _____

Words with *i* in Two Syllables

8. _____   12. _____
9. _____   13. _____
10. _____   14. _____
11. _____   15. _____

The Two Words That Did Not Fit in Any Other List

26. _____
27. _____

E. Generally Speaking Write each of the spelling words for the group it best fits.

1. area, section, _____
2. put in, place, _____
3. doctor, teeth, _____
4. feeling, urge, _____
5. salary, pay, _____
6. turn, bend, _____
7. aid, help, _____
8. end, boundary, _____
9. cutters, shears, _____
10. shoes, sandals, _____
11. pay later, charge, _____
12. playing time, round, _____
13. excuse, send away, _____
14. approved, allowed, _____
15. show, display, _____
16. allow in, accept as true, _____
17. demand, declare, _____
18. increase, gain, _____
19. liveliness, enthusiasm, _____
20. OK, consent, _____

Spelling Words

limit	*spirit*	*admit*	*credit*	*profit*
exhibit	*deposit*	*permitted*	*permission*	*twist*
assist	*insist*	*dentist*	*impulse*	*inning*
income	*dismiss*	*district*	*slippers*	*scissors*

F. Guide Words These word pairs are guide words that might appear in a dictionary. Write the words from the spelling list that would appear on the same page as each pair of guide words.

abandon – adventure

1. _____

assigned – boil

2. _____

concern – cushion

3. _____

customer – design

4. _____

5. _____

desire – document

6. _____

7. _____

evil – fault

8. _____

hesitate – insect

9. _____

10. _____

11. _____

insects – knowledge

12. _____

labor – machine

13. _____

perform – poultry

14. _____

15. _____

power – publish

16. _____

scarcely – sicken

17. _____

silent – staff

18. _____

19. _____

treatment – various

20. _____

G. Using Other Word Forms Write the Other Word Form (p. 112) that fits each group of words.

1. restricted, confined, _limited_ (limit)
2. confessed, acknowledged, _admitted_ (admit)
3. helped, aided, _assisted_ (assist)
4. showed, demonstrated, _exhibited_ (exhibit)
5. put down, placed for safekeeping, _deposited_ (deposit)

H. Challenge Words Write the Challenge Word that completes each phrase.

apprentice	considerable	discharge	epistle	quivering

1. not a small amount, but a _considerable_ amount
2. not still, but _quivering_
3. not an expert, but an _apprentice_
4. not enroll, but _discharge_
5. not a letter, but an _epistle_

I. Spelling and Writing Write the following phrases in sentences. Proofread your spelling.

Example: *They permitted him to design the costumes.*

1. permitted him
2. senator's district
3. pink slippers
4. income tax
5. visit the dentist
6. sharp scissors
7. received credit for
8. will dismiss us
9. he can insist
10. art exhibit
11. must admit
12. twist the cover
13. gave me permission
14. put a deposit on
15. in good spirit
16. on impulse
17. will profit from
18. the third inning
19. assist me with
20. limit the amount

29

A. Pretest Write each spelling word.

B. Spelling Words and Phrases

1.	**customer**	one to a <u>customer</u>
2.	**runaway**	<u>runaway</u> horse
3.	**submarine**	an atomic <u>submarine</u>
4.	**republic**	flag of the <u>republic</u>
5.	**instruction**	swimming <u>instruction</u>
6.	**difficult**	<u>difficult</u> to refuse
7.	**stomach**	<u>stomach</u> trouble
8.	**onion**	strong <u>onion</u> smell
9.	**countries**	neighboring <u>countries</u>
10.	**suitable**	<u>suitable</u> for framing
11.	**firm**	a <u>firm</u> handshake
12.	**thirsty**	<u>thirsty</u> hikers
13.	**Thursday**	to deliver on <u>Thursday</u>
14.	**purple**	a <u>purple</u> grape
15.	**burden**	a heavy <u>burden</u>
16.	**curtain**	closed the <u>curtain</u>
17.	**furniture**	outdoor <u>furniture</u>
18.	**courage**	known for <u>courage</u>
19.	**government**	<u>government</u> offices
20.	**otherwise**	will leave <u>otherwise</u>

Other Word Forms

customers	firmest, firmly
runaways	thirst, thirstily
submarines	Thurs.
republics	purpled, purplish
instruct, instructs,	burdens
instructor, instructions	curtains
difficulty, difficulties	furnish
stomachs	courageous
onions	govern, governs,
country	governing, governor,
suit, suitably	governments

C. Visual Warm-up Write each word in its correct shape.

a.

b.

c.

d.

e.

f.

g.

h.

i.

j.

k.

l.

m.

n.

o.

p.

q.

r.

s.

t.

D. All in a Row Write the twenty spelling words in alphabetical order. Then join the boxed letters and write four hidden words.

1. __ ☐ __ __ __ __
2. __ __ __ ☐ __ __ __ __ ☐
3. __ __ ☐ __ __ __ __
4. __ __ ☐ __ __ __
5. __ __ __ __ __ ☐ __
6. Hidden Word: _____
7. ☐ __ __ __ ☐ __ __ __
8. ☐ __ __ __
9. ☐ __ __
10. __ __ __ ☐ __ __ __ __
11. __ __ __ ☐ __ __ __ __ __
12. Hidden Word: _____

13. __ __ __ __ ☐ __
14. __ __ __ __ __ ☐ __ __ __ __
15. __ __ ☐ __ __ __ __
16. __ __ ☐ __ __ __ __ __ __
17. __ __ __ __ ☐ __ __ __
18. Hidden Word: _____
19. __ ☐ __ __ __ __
20. __ __ __ __ __ ☐ __ __ ☐
21. __ __ __ ☐ __ __
22. __ __ ☐ __ __ __ __
23. __ __ __ __ __ __ ☐
24. Hidden Word: _____

E. Base Words The spelling list contains fourteen base words and six words that are not base words. Write each spelling word.

Not Base Words	Base Words	Not Base Words	Base Words
1. firmly	_____	10. difficulty	_____
2. curtains	_____	11. republics	_____
3. submarines	_____	12. runaways	_____
4. onions	_____	13. _____	thirst
5. courageous	_____	14. _____	instruct
6. customers	_____	15. _____	suit
7. purpled	_____	16. _____	country
8. stomachs	_____	17. _____	govern
9. burdens	_____	18. _____	furnish

19. Write the two base words not used above. **a.** _____   **b.** _____

Spelling Words

customer	runaway	submarine	republic	instruction
difficult	stomach	onion	countries	suitable
firm	thirsty	Thursday	purple	burden
curtain	furniture	courage	government	otherwise

F. Crossword Puzzle Solve the puzzle by using all the words from the spelling list. Write the words. One word will be an Other Word Form (p. 116). Check your answers in the **Spelling Dictionary**.

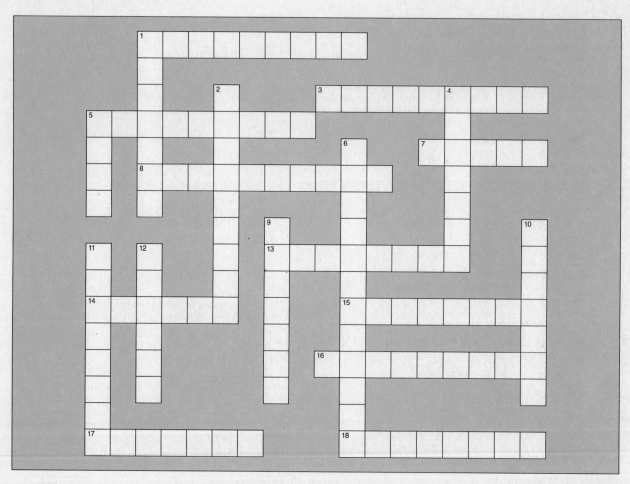

Across

1. France and Spain
3. an underwater vessel
5. tables and chairs
7. a vegetable
8. a country's system of rules
13. a day of the week
14. a dark color
15. one who makes a purchase
16. hard to do
17. a window covering
18. proper or fitting

Down

1. bravery
2. differently
4. out of control
5. unshaking; steady
6. lessons
9. the organ that digests food
10. needing water
11. a type of government
12. a load

G. Using Other Word Forms Write the Other Word Form (p. 116) that completes each sentence.

1. They shook hands _firmly_ (firm) after making the deal.

2. The painting has a _purplish_ (purple) background.

3. Our _govenor_ (government) has been in office for five years.

4. I am having _difficulty_ (difficult) with my math homework.

5. Please read the _instructions_ (instruction) carefully.

H. Challenge Words Write the Challenge Word that completes each sentence.

misjudge	observatories	sculptures	merciless	structures

1. Astronomers view stars from _observatories_ .

2. A wolverine can be a savage and _merciless_ animal.

3. The architect designs skyscrapers and other tall _structures_ .

4. A trapeze artist must never _misjudge_ the position of the trapeze.

5. The artist creates unique _sculptures_ from clay.

I. Spelling and Writing Write each set of words in a sentence. You may use Other Word Forms. Proofread your spelling.

Example: firm – Thursday
The mice ate the firm cheese on Thursday.

1. submarine – runaway – courage

2. otherwise – suitable – customer

3. difficult – instruction – burden

4. onion – stomach – thirsty

5. purple – furniture – curtain

6. republic – countries – government

30 REVIEWING LESSONS 25-29

■ freight	★ collect	▲ cabinet	◆ spirit	● Thursday
voyage	special	vanity	slippers	onion
channel	expense	catalog	dentist	thirsty
weight	insects	factories	admit	purple
lantern	gentle	material	scissors	stomach

A. Sentences in Paragraphs Write Other Word Forms or the spelling words to complete the sentences. Use the words under the first shape to complete the first paragraph, and so on. Write each word or its Other Word Form only once. If you need help, use the **Spelling Dictionary**.

■ A **(1.)** _____ is a large ship that makes **(2.)** _____ through waterways known as **(3.)** _____ . Every piece of cargo is **(4.)** _____ before being placed on board. Unlike ships long ago, freighters use electricity, not gas **(5.)** _____ .

★ Some people enjoy **(6.)** _____ rocks, stamps, and coins. There are shops which **(7.)** _____ in selling different collectors' items. Buying these items can be very **(8.)** _____ . I know of a person who purchased an addition for his **(9.)** _____ collection. He handles this insect very **(10.)** _____ , since it is his most expensive purchase.

▲ My cousins have a talent for carpentry work. Recently, they built new kitchen **(11.)** _____ for my aunt. My cousins are not boastful or **(12.)** _____ about their work. Sometimes they look through **(13.)** _____ for ideas. They plan to visit a cabinet **(14.)** _____ soon, so they can see how different wood **(15.)** _____ are used.

◆ With very low **(16.)** _____ , I usually **(17.)** _____ quietly into any **(18.)** _____ office. I have always **(19.)** _____ that I have a fear of sharp objects such as knives, **(20.)** _____ , and drills!

● On **(21.)** _____ , the cooks served sandwiches with **(22.)** _____ for lunch. Within one hour, we all had a **(23.)** _____ for water. Several students began turning a **(24.)** _____ color in history class and complained that their **(25.)** _____ were upset.

REVIEW

120 Review—Lesson 30

active	capital	expect	instruction	passage
affect	deposit	firm	joint	permission
assist	destroy	government	limit	respect
attractive	difficult	happiness	neglect	selfish
avoid	example	impulse	neighboring	suitable

B. Before and After

Find the spelling word that comes alphabetically right *before* each word below. Write the spelling word and an Other Word Form for each spelling word. If you need help, use the **Spelling Dictionary**.

Before	**Spelling Words**	**Other Word Forms**
1. neither	*neighboring*	*neighbors*
2. neighbor		
3. linen		
4. exchange		
5. patent		
6. senior		
7. awful		
8. flavor		
9. direct		
10. journey		
11. insure		
12. happy		

Now find the spelling word that comes alphabetically right *after* each word below. Write the spelling word and an Other Word Form for each spelling word.

After	**Spelling Words**	**Other Word Forms**
13. action		
14. dessert		
15. resort		
16. improvement		
17. govern		
18. suit		
19. advise		
20. department		
21. attract		
22. capable		
23. assigned		
24. permanent		
25. exhibit		

■ salad	★ traveler	▲ accept	◆ boiler	● accent
pattern	object	directed	method	velvet
abandon	battery	chapter	advertise	exhibit
submarine	twist	dismiss	permitted	curtain
credit	furniture	otherwise	customer	rapidly

C. Classified Ads

Decide how to complete each ad with Other Word Forms or the spelling words. Write the words. The shape tells you in what column you can find the spelling word. Use each word or its Other Word Form only once. If you need help, use the **Spelling Dictionary**.

1. Restaurant ad: No soggy green ■ _____ served.

2. Clothes designer ad: We pin ■ _____ perfectly.

3. Furnace repair shop ad: We're hot on mending ◆ _____ .

4. Language teacher ad: All ● _____ accepted.

5. Boat captain ad: We ★ _____ in waves.

6. Secondhand store ad: Our business is ▲ _____ your rejects.

7. Dime store ad: Odd ★ _____ are our specialty.

8. Barbershop ad: Two new ◆ _____ to end baldness.

9. Filmmaker ad: A ▲ _____ needed for reel-life drama.

10. Airline ad: Soft ● _____ seats make for soft landings.

11. Book writer ad: Ten ▲ _____ in ten days.

12. Zookeeper ad: Caretakers wanted for ■ _____ anteaters.

13. Bus tour ad: As ◆ _____ , discount rates start this week.

14. Gas station ad: We charge ★ _____ for free.

15. Computer company ad: Visit both ● _____ ; we need your input.

16. School ad: Enroll at our school; daily ▲ _____ guaranteed.

17. Pasta maker ad: We teach spaghetti ★ _____ to teens.

18. Sailor ad: Need water for ■ _____ ; ▲ _____ we walk.

19. State park ad: Picknicking ◆ _____ required.

20. Mirror and glass store ad: Our best ◆ _____ are window shoppers.

21. Cabinet maker ad: Fancy ★ _____ made while you wait.

22. Window store ad: Corduroy ● _____ come pleated.

23. Track team ad: Very ● _____ runners required.

24. Discount store ad: Your ■ _____ is good but your cash is better.

■ traffic	★ accident	▲ courage	◆ lettuce	● defense
seldom	profit	inning	republic	practical
countries	loyal	patent	advantage	runaway
spoil	metal	exactly	athlete	action
insist	burden	whether	district	income

D. Words in a Series Decide how to use Other Word Forms or the spelling words to complete each series. Write the words. The shape tells you in what column you can find the spelling word. Use each word or its Other Word Form only once.

1. greens, cabbage, ◆ _____

2. cars, buses, ■ _____

3. governments, democracies, ◆ _____

4. unplanned, unintended, ★ _____

5. bravery, fearlessness, ▲ _____

6. powerless, helpless, ● _____

7. actually, sensibly, ● _____

8. rarely, hardly, ■ _____

9. region, state, ■ _____

10. gains, rewards, ★ _____

11. periods, quarters, ▲ _____

12. invented, created, ▲ _____

13. trueness, faithfulness, ★ _____

14. correct, right, ▲ _____

15. benefits, gains, ◆ _____

16. stowaways, stampeding animals, ● _____

17. decayed, rotten, ■ _____

18. ores, minerals, ★ _____

19. ballplayers, swimmers, ◆ _____

20. movements, deeds, ● _____

21. earnings, salaries, ● _____

22. areas, sections, ◆ _____

23. weights, loads, ★ _____

24. demands, requires, ■ _____

25. either, if, ▲ _____

Working Words in Spelling **123**

31

A. Pretest Write each spelling word.

B. Spelling Words and Phrases

1.	enemies	friends or enemies
2.	envelope	a stamped envelope
3.	elevator	elevator to the lobby
4.	exercise	an exercise bicycle
5.	express	shipped by express
6.	extent	the extent of the trouble
7.	prevent	to prevent the theft
8.	cement	cement wall
9.	element	an important element
10.	settlement	to build a settlement
11.	independent	an independent person
12.	represent	will represent the owner
13.	presented	presented an award
14.	memory	lost my memory
15.	membership	membership in a club
16.	century	turn of the century
17.	several	several oval shapes
18.	skeleton	skeleton bones
19.	reckless	needlessly reckless
20.	arrest	under arrest

Other Word Forms

enemy	independently
envelopes	representing,
elevate, elevating	representative,
exercises, exercising	representation
expresses, expressing,	present, presenting,
expression	presentation
extend, extents, extension	memories
prevented, preventative,	member, memberships
prevention	centuries
cemented, cementing	skeletons
elements	recklessly
settle, settling	arrests, arresting

C. Visual Warm-up Write each word in its correct shape.

a.

b.

c.

d.

e.

f.

g.

h.

i.

j.

k.

l.

m.

n.

o.

p.

q.

r.

s.

t.

D. Sort Your _E_'s Each word in the spelling list has at least one _e_. Write each word where it belongs.

One _e_

1. _____ 2. _____ 3. _____

Two _e_'s

4. _____ 7. _____ 10. _____

5. _____ 8. _____ 11. _____

6. _____ 9. _____ 12. _____

Three _e_'s

13. _____ 16. _____ 19. _____

14. _____ 17. _____ 20. _____

15. _____ 18. _____

E. Bases and Suffixes The spelling list contains fifteen base words and five words with suffixes. Write each spelling word.

Words with Suffixes	Base Words	Words with Suffixes	Base Words
1. extents	_____	11. exercises	_____
2. skeletons	_____	12. elements	_____
3. cementing	_____	13. recklessly	_____
4. representative	_____	14. centuries	_____
5. expressing	_____	15. _____	present
6. prevention	_____	16. _____	settle
7. envelopes	_____	17. _____	elevate
8. memories	_____	18. _____	enemy
9. independently	_____	19. _____	member
10. arresting	_____		

20. Write the one base word not used above. _____

Spelling Words

enemies	envelope	elevator	exercise	express
extent	prevent	cement	element	settlement
independent	represent	presented	memory	membership
century	several	skeleton	reckless	arrest

F. What's the Suggestion? Write a word from the spelling list for each suggestion.

1. One word suggests bones: _____

2. One word suggests dues: _____

3. One word suggests police officer: _____

4. One word suggests daredevil: _____

5. One word suggests hundred: _____

6. One word suggests push-ups: _____

7. One word suggests chemical substance: _____

8. One word suggests postage: _____

9. One word suggests remembering: _____

10. One word suggests colony: _____

11. One word suggests alone: _____

12. One word suggests glue: _____

13. One word suggests rapid train: _____

14. One word suggests up and down: _____

15. One word suggests some: _____

16. One word suggests given: _____

17. One word suggests lawyer: _____

18. One word suggests stopping: _____

19. One word suggests distance: _____

20. One word suggests hateful people: _____

G. Using Other Word Forms Write the Other Word Form (p. 124) that fits each clue.

1. a saying _____ (express)

2. working out _____ (exercise)

3. experiences that are remembered _____ (memory)

4. groups of one hundred years _____ (century)

5. a demonstration or showing _____ (presented)

H. Challenge Words Write the Challenge Word that completes each analogy.

elementary	requested	generous	reception	subsequent

1. selfish is to **stingy** as **unselfish** is to _____

2. deceive is to **deception** as **receive** is to _____

3. answered is to **asked** as **responded** is to _____

4. early is to **later** as **prior** is to _____

5. complex is to **advanced** as **simple** is to _____

I. Spelling and Writing Use as many of the Spelling Words, Other Word Forms, and Challenge Words as you can to write some imaginary newspaper headlines. Then circle the spelling words you used. Proofread your spelling.

Example: *Team* (*Memberships*) (*Present*) *Active* (*Exercise*).

32

A. Pretest Write each spelling word.

B. Spelling Words and Phrases

1.	strict	strict but fair
2.	stingy	selfish and stingy
3.	pity	filled with pity
4.	simply	simply made
5.	misery	misery and fever
6.	mineral	mineral water
7.	citizen	Canadian citizen
8.	prisoner	prisoner of war
9.	victory	the glory of victory
10.	dictionary	heavy dictionary
11.	division	long division
12.	provisions	carried provisions
13.	admission	paid admission
14.	ability	ability to win
15.	activity	sports activity
16.	delivery	delivery truck
17.	continue	will continue the work
18.	submit	to submit a report
19.	impossible	impossible mission
20.	business	electronics business

Other Word Forms

strictly
stingier, stingiest
pities, pitying, pitiful
simple, simplest,
  simplicity
miseries, miserable
minerals
citizenship
prison
victories, victorious
dictionaries
divide, dividing

provide, provided, providing
admit, admitting,
  admittance
abilities
active, activities
delivering, deliveries
continues, continued,
  continuous
submitted
possible, impossibly,
  impossibility
busy, businesses

C. Visual Warm-up Write each word in its correct shape.

a.

b.

c.

d.

e.

f.

g.

h.

i.

j.

k.

l.

m.

n.

o.

p.

q.

r.

s.

t.

D. Sort Your Vowels Write each spelling word where it belongs.

1. Write the nine words with a long *e* sound spelled *y*.

a. _____   d. _____   g. _____

b. _____   e. _____   h. _____

c. _____   f. _____   i. _____

2. Write the five words *not* used above with two or more *i*'s.

a. _____   c. _____   e. _____

b. _____   d. _____

3. Write the remaining six words with a short *i* sound.

a. _____   c. _____   e. _____

b. _____   d. _____   f. _____

E. Guide Words These word pairs are guide words that might appear in a dictionary. Write the words from the spelling list that would appear on the same page as each pair of guide words.

abandon – adventure	**desire – document**	**power – publish**
1. _____	8. _____	14. _____
2. _____	9. _____	15. _____
3. _____		
	hesitate – insect	**silent – succeed**
boiler – chalk	10. _____	16. _____
4. _____		17. _____
	machinery – poultry	18. _____
chamber – design	11. _____	19. _____
5. _____	12. _____	
6. _____	13. _____	**vary – wrench**
7. _____		20. _____

Spelling Words

strict	stingy	pity	simply	misery
mineral	citizen	prisoner	victory	dictionary
division	provisions	admission	ability	activity
delivery	continue	submit	impossible	business

F. Generally Speaking Write the spelling word that best fits each group or phrase below.

1. company, store, _____

2. alphabetical word book, _____

3. go on, proceed, _____

4. separation, section, _____

5. entrance fee, price, _____

6. native, resident, _____

7. ungenerous, scanty, _____

8. captive, convict, _____

9. hopeless, unthinkable, _____

10. project, game, _____

11. talent, skill _____

12. easily, plainly, _____

13. suffering, unhappiness, _____

14. win, success, _____

15. metal, ore, _____

16. package, distribution, _____

17. sorrow, sympathy, _____

18. food, supplies, _____

19. stern, firm, _____

20. surrender, give up, _____

G. Using Other Word Forms Write the Other Word Form (p. 128) that completes each sentence.

1. The team has won many _____ (victory) this season.

2. The sad dog is such a _____ (pity) sight.

3. The driver has made eight _____ (delivery) today.

4. We'll need _____ (dictionary) to do the vocabulary exercises.

5. That selfish man is the _____ (stingy) person I know.

H. Challenge Words Write the Challenge Word that replaces the underlined word or words.

immortal	ingredients	intestine	missiles	predicted

1. The emperor believes that he is going to live forever. _____

2. Each country constructed guided weapons. _____

3. The fortune teller claims to have foretold the future. _____

4. The recipe calls for many elements to be added. _____

5. Her pain is due to a blockage in her digestive column. _____

I. Spelling and Writing Use as many of the Spelling Words, Other Word Forms, and Challenge Words as you can to make up titles for books. Then circle the spelling words you used. Proofread your spelling.

Example: (Strictly) (Business)

33

A. Pretest Write each spelling word.

B. Spelling Words and Phrases

1.	author	a wordy author
2.	auction	used-car auction
3.	caution	will enter with caution
4.	fault	your fault
5.	pause	to pause to breathe
6.	launch	to launch a rocket
7.	laundry	dirty laundry
8.	thoughtful	looking thoughtful
9.	chalk	eraser and chalk
10.	awfully	awfully upset
11.	awkward	an awkward move
12.	lawyers	books for lawyers
13.	opera	opera singer
14.	colonies	colonies of insects
15.	positive	positive or negative
16.	opposite	not opposite but similar
17.	knowledge	scientific knowledge
18.	astonished	astonished by the news
19.	squash	squash on the vine
20.	vacant	a vacant lot

Other Word Forms

authors	lawyer
auctions, auctioned,	operas
auctioneer	colony, colonist,
cautioning, cautious	colonize
faults, faulty	positively
pauses, paused, pausing	oppose, opposites
launches, launched,	knowledgeable
launching	astonish, astonishes,
laundries	astonishing,
think, thinking, thought	astonishment
chalky	squashes, squashed
awful	vacate, vacating,
awkwardly	vacancy, vacantly

C. Visual Warm-up Write each word in its correct shape.

a.

b.

c.

d.

e.

f.

g.

h.

i.

j.

k.

l.

m.

n.

o.

p.

q.

r.

s.

t.

D. Across and Down The spelling words can be found in the word puzzle. The words appear across and down. Circle and write the words.

Across

1. _____

2. _____

3. _____

4. _____

5. _____

6. _____

7. _____

8. _____

9. _____

10. _____

11. _____

12. _____

```
l p m f o n a l a w y e r s r
s q u a s h s c o p i n y o n
j u k u r s t l a u n c h p y
i h v l t u o p p o s i t e k
a u c t i o n c h a l k b r n
g w c a u t i o n q u a c a o
a a f b c d s r a p a u s e w
w w v w u t h o u g h t f u l
k f a a l t e t t j f h k d e
w u c l q u d d h i g m e b d
a l a o p c o l o n i e s n g
r l n l a u n d r y c p d a e
d y t y z o p o s i t i v e v
```

Down

13. _____

14. _____

15. _____

16. _____

17. _____

18. _____

19. _____

20. _____

E. Not _____, But Write the spelling word that best fits each phrase.

1. not to continue, but to _____

2. not negative, but _____

3. not ignorance, but _____

4. not carelessly, but with _____

5. not unthinking, but _____

6. not the same, but the _____

7. not to land, but to _____

8. not graceful, but _____

9. not crayons, but _____

10. not filled, but _____

Spelling Words

author	auction	caution	fault	pause
launch	laundry	thoughtful	chalk	awfully
awkward	lawyers	opera	colonies	positive
opposite	knowledge	astonished	squash	vacant

F. Bases and Suffixes The spelling list contains fourteen base words and six words and suffixes. Write each spelling word.

Words with Suffixes   **Base Words**

1. positively   _____

2. auctions   _____

3. launching   _____

4. faulty   _____

5. chalky   _____

6. squashed   _____

7. cautioning   _____

8. authors   _____

9. paused   _____

10. operas   _____

11. vacantly   _____

12. awkwardly   _____

13. laundries   _____

14. knowledgeable   _____

15. _____ thought

16. _____ lawyer

17. _____ colony

18. _____ astonish

19. _____ oppose

20. _____ awful

G. Using Other Word Forms Write the Other Word Form (p. 132) that replaces each underlined word or phrase.

1. The speaker <u>stopped briefly</u> until the crowd was quiet.   _____ (pause)

2. Our neighbors are <u>leaving</u> their house today.   _____ (vacant)

3. A <u>careful</u> driver slows down for sharp curves.   _____ (caution)

4. The puppy runs very <u>clumsily</u>.   _____ (awkward)

5. That story is <u>very surprising</u>.   _____ (astonished)

H. Challenge Words Write the Challenge Word that completes each group of words.

authentic	moderate	conquered	resolved	wrought

1. reasonable, temperate, _____

2. defeated, overcame, _____

3. concluded, decided, _____

4. genuine, real, _____

5. put together, hammered, _____

I. Spelling and Writing Use as many of the Spelling Words, Other Word Forms, and Challenge Words as you can in sentences about one of the following titles. Then circle the spelling words you used. Proofread your spelling.

<u>The Underwater Cave</u> or <u>The Lost Baseball</u>

Example: *The (awkward) diver (astonished) the (thoughtful) whale.*

34

A. Pretest Write each spelling word.

B. Spelling Words and Phrases

1. doubt — without a <u>doubt</u>
2. account — a bank <u>account</u>
3. towel — <u>towel</u> rack
4. powerful — a <u>powerful</u> motor
5. approve — will <u>approve</u> the changes
6. improvement — saw the <u>improvement</u>
7. woolen — <u>woolen</u> sweater
8. fully — agreed <u>fully</u>
9. bushel — <u>bushel</u> basket
10. cushion — soft <u>cushion</u>
11. document — a legal <u>document</u>
12. glitter — the gold's <u>glitter</u>
13. differ — seemed to <u>differ</u>
14. familiar — similar and <u>familiar</u>
15. connection — in <u>connection</u> with
16. concerned — a very <u>concerned</u> friend
17. harmony — in perfect <u>harmony</u>
18. expose — to <u>expose</u> to the sun
19. assigned — <u>assigned</u> work
20. muscle — flexed a <u>muscle</u>

Other Word Forms

doubted, doubtful	documentary
accounts, accounting, accountant	glittered, glittery
	differed, different
towels	familiarize
power, powerfully	connected, connecting
approved, approving, approval	concerning
improve, improved, improving	harmonize, harmonious
wool	exposes, exposing, exposure
full	assign, assignment
bushels	muscles, muscular
cushions, cushioned	

C. Visual Warm-up Write each word in its correct shape.

a.
b.
c.
d.
e.
f.
g.
h.
i.
j.
k.
l.
m.
n.
o.
p.
q.
r.
s.
t.

D. Generally Speaking Write the spelling word for the group it best fits.

1. bank record, deposit, _____

2. 4 pecks, 32 quarts, _____

3. record, certificate, _____

4. mistrust, question, _____

5. uncover, lay open, _____

6. completely, wholly, _____

7. placed, appointed, _____

8. washcloth, blanket, _____

9. correction, change, _____

10. body tissue, strength, _____

11. silk, cotton, _____

12. known, common, _____

13. pillow, pad, _____

14. link, union, _____

15. melody, song, _____

16. accept, OK, _____

17. strong, forceful, _____

18. vary, disagree, _____

19. shine, sparkle, _____

20. troubled, worried, _____

E. Guide Words These word pairs are guide words that might appear in a dictionary. Write the words from the spelling list that would appear on the same page as each pair of guide words.

abandon – assign

1. _____

2. _____

assigned – boil

3. _____

boiler – chalk

4. _____

concern – cushion

5. _____

6. _____

7. _____

desire – document

8. _____

9. _____

doubt – estate

10. _____

evil – fault

11. _____

12. _____

favor – future

13. _____

gallop – height

14. _____

15. _____

hesitate – publish

16. _____

17. _____

18. _____

theater – wrench

19. _____

20. _____

Spelling Words

doubt	account	towel	powerful	approve
improvement	woolen	fully	bushel	cushion
document	glitter	differ	familiar	connection
concerned	harmony	expose	assigned	muscle

F. Crossword Puzzle Solve the puzzle by using all the words from the spelling list. Write the words. Check your answers in the **Spelling Dictionary**.

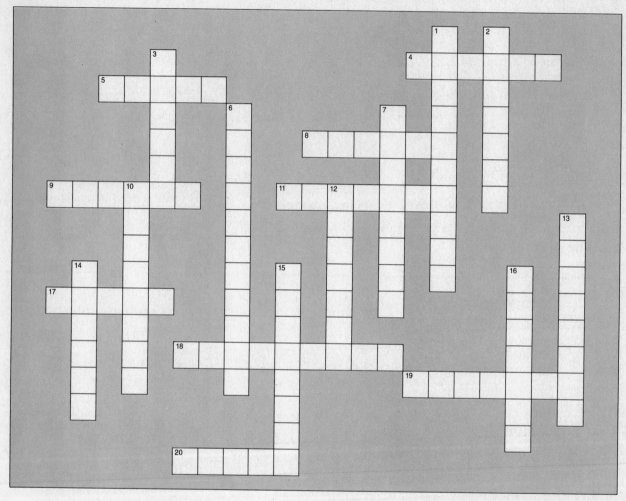

Across

4. of wool
5. to be unsure
8. to lay open; uncover
9. to be unalike
11. a bank record
17. completely
18. worried
19. to OK
20. used to dry dishes

Down

1. a link
2. to sparkle
3. provides arm movement
6. something better
7. an official paper
10. known
12. a soft pillow
13. appointed; placed
14. four pecks
15. strong
16. a blending of musical sounds

G. Using Other Word Forms Write the Other Word Form (p. 136) that completes each series.

1. approves, approved, _____

2. connects, _____ , connecting

3. cushions, _____ , cushioning

4. accounts, accounted, _____

5. improves, improved, _____

H. Challenge Words Write the Challenge Word that completes each phrase.

parcel post	conceive	Olympic	propeller	trousers

1. imagine or _____

2. revolving blade or _____

3. pants or _____

4. air mail or _____

5. international competition or _____ competition

I. Spelling and Writing Write in your journal. Use as many of the Spelling Words, Other Word Forms and Challenge Words as you can to write a page about the day school was cancelled. Then circle the spelling words you used. Remember when writing a journal to include the date, the time, and what happened. Proofread your spelling.

Example: *November 29—9:30—There was no (doubt) in my mind that school would be cancelled today.*

35

A. Pretest Write each spelling word.

B. Spelling Words and Phrases

1.	cultivate	hard to <u>cultivate</u>
2.	separate	<u>separate</u> tables
3.	decorate	will <u>decorate</u> the room
4.	hesitate	made me <u>hesitate</u>
5.	relative	not a close <u>relative</u>
6.	election	<u>election</u> of the mayor
7.	selection	a varied <u>selection</u>
8.	direction	which <u>direction</u> to take
9.	inspection	<u>inspection</u> time for cars
10.	attention	<u>attention</u> to detail
11.	invention	a simple <u>invention</u>
12.	convention	political <u>convention</u>
13.	assembly	a student <u>assembly</u>
14.	amendment	to make an <u>amendment</u>
15.	vegetable	a fresh <u>vegetable</u>
16.	necessary	<u>necessary</u> to do
17.	telegraph	<u>telegraph</u> message
18.	telephone	my own <u>telephone</u>
19.	television	the <u>television</u> program
20.	against	leaned <u>against</u> the wall

Other Word Forms

cultivated, cultivating, cultivation	attend, attentive
	invented, inventor
separating, separation	conventions
decorating, decoration, decorator	assemble, assembling, assemblies
hesitated, hesitation	amend, amended
relate, relating, relation	vegetables
elect, elected	necessarily
select	telegraphed
direct, directed, director	telephoning
inspect, inspected, inspector	televise, televisions

C. Visual Warm-up Write each word in its correct shape.

a.

b.

c.

d.

e.

f.

g.

h.

i.

j.

k.

l.

m.

n.

o.

p.

q.

r.

s.

t.

D. Word Riddles Write the answer to each question with a <u>tion</u>, <u>tele</u>, or an <u>ate</u> word from the spelling list.

1. What <u>tion</u> tells how? _____

2. What <u>tion</u> is a close look? _____

3. What <u>tion</u> is a large meeting? _____

4. What <u>tion</u> selects our leaders? _____

5. What <u>tion</u> is careful listening? _____

6. What <u>tion</u> is a choice? _____

7. What <u>tion</u> is something new? _____

8. What <u>tele</u> calls a friend? _____

9. What <u>tele</u> entertains? _____

10. What <u>tele</u> sends a message? _____

11. What <u>ate</u> is to pause? _____

12. What <u>ate</u> is to plow soil? _____

13. What <u>ate</u> is to make a pretty room? _____

14. What <u>ate</u> is to divide? _____

15. Write the six words that were not used above.

a. _____ **c.** _____ **e.** _____

b. _____ **d.** _____ **f.** _____

E. Be a Word Detective Find the missing vowels and write the spelling words.

1. __ g __ __ nst   _____

2. s __ p __ r __ te   _____

3. __ m __ ndm __ nt   _____

4. v __ g __ t __ bl __   _____

5. c __ nv __ nt __ __ n   _____

6. __ l __ ct __ __ n   _____

7. c __ lt __ v __ t __   _____

8. s __ l __ ct __ __ n   _____

Spelling Words

cultivate	separate	decorate	hesitate	relative
election	selection	direction	inspection	attention
invention	convention	assembly	amendment	vegetable
necessary	telegraph	telephone	television	against

F. Guide Words These word pairs are guide words that might appear in a dictionary. Write the words from the spelling list that would appear on the same page as each pair of guide words.

assembly – assign

1. _____

2. _____

3. _____

assigned – boil

4. _____

concern – cushion

5. _____

6. _____

customer – design

7. _____

desire – document

8. _____

doubt – estate

9. _____

hesitate – insect

10. _____

insects – knowledge

11. _____

12. _____

minor – nowhere

13. _____

regard – scarce

14. _____

scarcely – sicken

15. _____

16. _____

sudden – terror

17. _____

18. _____

19. _____

vary – wrench

20. _____

G. Using Other Word Forms Write the Other Word Form (p. 140) that completes each sentence.

1. My brother is putting together the bicycle. He is _____ (assembly) it.

2. The oil and vinegar are coming apart. They are _____ (separate).

3. The baker is putting icing on the cake. She is _____ (decorate) it.

4. They will be farming that land this spring. They will be _____ (cultivate) it.

5. The club chose a new leader. A president was _____ (election).

H. Challenge Words Write the Challenge Word that completes each analogy.

elderly	identical	consequence	density	magnetic

1. **solid** is to **solidity** as **dense** is to _____

2. **young** is to **youthful** as **old** is to _____

3. **unlike** is to **different** as **same** is to _____

4. **repel** is to **repulsive** as **attract** is to _____

5. **action** is to **reaction** as **cause** is to _____

I. Spelling and Writing Write the following phrases in sentences. Proofread your spelling.

Example: *They gathered together for the yearly convention.*

1. yearly convention
2. local election
3. rotten vegetable
4. colored television
5. had to separate
6. school assembly
7. dead telephone
8. secret amendment
9. special inspection
10. can cultivate a garden
11. dangerous invention
12. complete attention
13. will hesitate too long
14. wrong direction
15. against the wind
16. interesting selection
17. completely necessary
18. distant relative
19. telegraph operator
20. will decorate the room

amendment	differ	fully	opposite	represent
awkward	election	inspection	pause	skeleton
bushel	element	invention	pity	strict
connection	extent	launch	powerful	victory
decorate	fault	memory	relative	woolen

A. Break the Code Use the code to write an Other Word Form for each spelling word. Write each word.

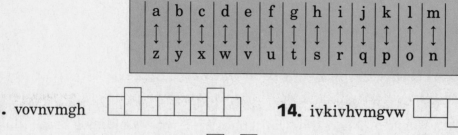

1. vovnvmgh

2. rmhkvxgvw

3. yfhsvoh

4. hgirxgob

5. xlmmvxgvw

6. rmevmgrmt

7. ufoo

8. kzfhvh

9. lkklhv

10. znvmwvw

11. hpvovgzo

12. krgrvh

13. ozfmxsrmt

14. ivkivhvmgvw

15. wvxlizgrlm

16. wruuvivmg

17. zdpdziwob

18. erxglirlfh

19. nvnlirav

20. kldviufoob

21. vovxgh

22. dllob

23. ivozgvw

24. uzfogh

25. vcgvmwvw

■ membership   ★ envelope   ▲ century   ◆ exercise   ● settlement

■	★	▲	◆	●
membership	envelope	century	exercise	settlement
selection	activity	dictionary	laundry	delivery
against	lawyers	vegetable	provisions	towel
positive	telegraph	assembly	opera	glitter
squash	mineral	improvement	assigned	muscle

B. Raising Questions Complete each question by writing Other Word Forms or the spelling words. The shape tells you in what column you can find the spelling word. Use each word or its Other Word Form only once. If you need help, use the **Spelling Dictionary**.

1. Were the ■ _____ given sealed ★ _____ to open?

2. How many ▲ _____ have passed since the Pilgrims ● _____ in Plymouth?

3. Are gymnastic ◆ _____ one of the ★ _____ offered after school?

4. Were the ▲ _____ for the English class ● _____ on time?

5. Did you ■ _____ ripe ▲ _____ from the garden?

6. Why did the ★ _____ bring his dirty ◆ _____ to court?

7. Are the wet ● _____ hanging ■ _____ the wall?

8. In 1844, did government officials ▲ _____ to watch as Samuel Morse ★ _____ his first message?

9. Is the hotel manager ■ _____ certain that he can ◆ _____ all the food?

10. Was the ◆ _____ singer wearing ■ _____ or cucumbers on her hat?

11. Did anyone in the science class know why the stones and ★ _____ were ● _____ in the dark?

12. Has the teacher asked you to ▲ _____ your written ◆ _____ on the ● _____ system?

■ vacant	★ hesitate	▲ elevator	◆ cultivate	● business
approve	chalk	prisoner	awfully	caution
cement	cushion	misery	presented	direction
citizen	telephone	continue	prevent	submit
doubt	arrest	thoughtful	separate	account

C. Sentences in Paragraphs Write Other Word Forms or the spelling words to complete the blanks. Use the words under the first shape to complete the first paragraph, and so on. Write each word or its Other Word Form only once. If you need help, use the **Spelling Dictionary**.

■   While the old hotel is crumbling, its **(1.)** _____ sign still hangs proudly. The holes in the walls provide homes for woodland animals. The mayor of the town has **(2.)** _____ a plan to have all the holes **(3.)** _____ . Yet, concerned **(4.)** _____ are expressing their **(5.)** _____ about this plan because they fear the animals will be injured.

★   The thieves **(6.)** _____ to steal the supplies of **(7.)** _____ from the school. They had already taken **(8.)** _____ and **(9.)** _____ from the school lobby and were afraid of being **(10.)** _____ .

▲   All of the **(11.)** _____ stopped with a jolt. We imagined ourselves as **(12.)** _____ with no escape. It was a **(13.)** _____ feeling at first, but we **(14.)** _____ to **(15.)** _____ positively about being rescued.

◆   Farmers work very hard **(16.)** _____ their land. Frequently, the **(17.)** _____ problem of having a poor mixture of soil **(18.)** _____ itself. When it is time to plant the crops, delays are **(19.)** _____ by first **(20.)** _____ the soil.

●   When dealing with all customers and **(21.)** _____ , bankers are very **(22.)** _____ . They often guide and **(23.)** _____ borrowers in the **(24.)** _____ of forms to apply for loans. Also, they check to make sure the numbers of all **(25.)** _____ are correct.

■ familiar ★ enemies ▲ independent ◆ auction ● colonies
express   document   several   reckless   impossible
colony   ability   convention   expose   harmony
stingy   simply   division   necessary   concerned
attention   astonished   author   admission   television

D. S-t-r-e-t-c-h the Meaning Write Other Word Forms or the spelling words to stretch the words and their meanings. The shape tells you in what column you can find the spelling word. Write each word or its Other Word Form only once. If you need help, use the **Spelling Dictionary**.

1. places where old, ■ _____ items are sold: ◆ _____

2. a person who ■ _____ bad feelings: ★ _____

3. a place where early settlers sought ▲ _____ : ● _____

4. ★ _____ that permit you to test all of your ★ _____ at catching minnows: fishing licenses

5. public meetings where ▲ _____ candidates are selected: ▲ _____ .

6. a ★ _____ math operation that gives you half the value of a number: ▲ _____ by two

7. singing more than one musical chord that is an ● _____ without two or more voices: ● _____

8. people who had ● _____ about settling in early America: ■ _____

9. the behavior of one who does not spend money ◆ _____ : ■ _____

10. people who ■ _____ to the matter of writing: ▲ _____

11. an act by a magician who never ◆ _____ the secret to the audience: ★ _____ trick

12. one of life's ◆ _____ : food

13. devices that display images on a screen: ● _____

14. a place you first go when entering a hospital: ◆ _____ room

Spelling Dictionary/WORDFINDER

Your Spelling Dictionary/WORDFINDER lists all the basic spelling words and Other Word Forms in your spelling book. If the entry word is a spelling word, it is listed in **dark type**. If the entry word is not in dark type, then the spelling word is listed with the Other Word Forms at the end of the definition.

The Spelling Dictionary/WORDFINDER gives you a quick way to check the spelling and meanings of your spelling words. Because the Spelling Dictionary/WORDFINDER includes many of the words you will need in daily writing, you will find it useful for other schoolwork too.

Sample entries —

invitation | ĭn′vĭ **tā′**shən | *n.* A polite request to come somewhere: *an invitation to visit.* [see *invite*]

invite | ĭn **vīt′** | *v.* To ask someone politely to come somewhere: *will invite them to dinner.* ***invites, invited, inviting, invitation, invitations*** — Other Word Forms

---

PRONUNCIATION KEY

ă	pat	j	judge	sh	dish, ship
ā	aid, fey, pay	k	cat, kick, pique	t	tight
â	air, care, wear	l	lid, needle	th	path, thin
ä	father	m	am, man, mum	*th*	bathe, this
b	bib	n	no, sudden	ŭ	cut, rough
ch	church	ng	thing	û	circle, firm, heard,
d	deed	ŏ	horrible, pot		term, turn, urge, word
ĕ	pet, pleasure	ō	go, hoarse, row, toe	v	cave, valve, vine
ē	be, bee, easy, leisure	ô	alter, caught, for, paw	w	with
f	fast, fife, off, phase, rough	oi	boy, noise, oil	y	yes
g	gag	ou	cow, out	yōō	abuse, use
h	hat	ōŏ	took	z	rose, size, xylophone, zebra
hw	which	ōō	boot, fruit	zh	garage, pleasure, vision
ĭ	pit	p	pop	ə	about, silent, pencil
ī	by, guy, pie	r	roar		lemon, circus
î	dear, deer, fierce, mere	s	miss, sauce, see	ər	butter

STRESS
Primary stress ′ **bi•ol′o•gy** |bī ŏl′ə jē| Secondary stress ′ **bi′o•log′i•cal** |bī′ə lŏj′ĭ kəl|

A

abandon | ə **băn′**dən | v. **1.** To leave or desert: *to abandon the car.* **2.** To give up completely: *will abandon the old idea.* **abandons, abandoned, abandoning, abandonment**

ability | ə **bĭl′**ĭ tē | n. The talent to do something; skillfulness: *excellent ability.* **abilities**

abroad | ə **brôd′** | adv. Outside one's land; to a foreign place: *will travel abroad.*

accent | **ăk′**sĕnt′ | n. A way of pronunciation in a certain area of a country: *a northern accent.* **accents, accented, accenting**

accept | ăk **sĕpt′** | v. To receive what is offered or given; agree to take: *will accept the gift.* **accepts, accepted, accepting, acceptable, acceptably, acceptant, acceptance, acceptability, accepter**

accident | **ăk′**sĭ dənt | n. Something unfortunate that happens: *a train accident.* **accidents, accidental, accidentally**

accord | ə **kôrd′** | v. To be in agreement with: *if the stories accord with each other.* **accords, accorded, according, accordingly, accordance**

according | ə **kôr′**dĭng | —**According to**—As stated by; as shown by. [see *accord*]

account | ə **kount′** | n. A record of money saved, exchanged, or owed: *opened an account.* **accounts, accounted, accounting, accountable, accountant**

ache | āk | n. A continuous pain: *a knee ache.* v. To suffer pain; be in pain: *if your legs ache.* **aches, ached, aching**

acid | **ăs′**ĭd | adj. Sour: *an acid flavor.* n. A compound that gives off hydrogen ions when mixed with water: *the solution of acid.* **acids, acidic, acidly, acidity, acidness**

acre | **ā′**kər | n. A unit measurement of land area equaling 160 square rods, or 43,560 square feet: *an acre of forest.* **acres, acreage**

action | **ăk′**shən | n. Motion or activity: *a sudden action.* **actions**

active | **ăk′**tĭv | adj. **1.** Busy: *an active day.* **2.** Showing much movement: *an active ball game.* **actively, activate, activates, activated, activating, activeness, activity, activities**

activity | ăk **tĭv′**ĭ tē | n. **1.** An organized event or thing to do: *a school activity.* **2.** An action or motion: *a tiring activity.* [see *active*]

adjust | ə **jŭst′** | v. **1.** To regulate or put in a position for proper functioning: *to adjust the lens.* **2.** To move into proper position: *to adjust the radio dial.* **adjusts, adjusted, adjusting, adjustable, adjustment, adjuster**

admire | ăd **mīr′** | v. To look at with wonder or pleasure: *will admire the painting.* **admires, admired, admiring, admiringly, admirable, admirer, admiration**

admission | ăd **mĭsh′**ən | n. The amount paid for the right to enter: *charged admission.* [see *admit*]

admit | ăd **mĭt′** | v. **1.** To accept that something is true: *will admit his error.* **2.** To allow in: *to admit several people.* **admits, admitted, admitting, admittedly, admittance, admission, admissions**

adopt | ə **dŏpt′** | v. **1.** To take as one's own: *to adopt the baby.* **2.** To accept others' ways as one's own: *may adopt their beliefs.* **adopts, adopted, adopting, adoptable, adopter, adoption**

advance | ăd **văns′** | adj. Early: *an advance warning.* n. A forward motion: *made a very slow advance.* **advances, advanced, advancing, advancer, advancement**

advantage | ăd **văn′**tĭj | n. Anything that benefits one: *a special advantage.* —**Take advantage of**—To benefit by. **advantages, advantageous, advantageously**

adventure | ăd **vĕn′**chər | adj. Of or related to an adventure: *saw an adventure movie.* n. A thrilling experience: *a wilderness adventure.* **adventures, adventured, adventuring, adventurer, adventurous, adventurously, adventuresome**

advertise | **ăd′**vər tīz′ | v. To announce publicly the qualities of something to help its sale: *advertise the bicycles.* **advertises, advertised, advertising, advertisement, advertiser**

advice | ăd **vīs′** | n. A suggestion about doing something: *helpful advice.* [see *advise*]

advise | ăd **vīz′** | v. To offer advice or give an opinion: *will advise them.* **advises, advised, advising, adviser, advice**

affect | ə **fĕkt′** | v. To change or influence: *can't affect the weather.* – | **ăf′**ĕkt | n. Feeling or emotion: *showed a great deal of affect.* **affects, affected, affecting**

against | ə **gĕnst′** | prep. **1.** To touch or come in contact with: *rubs against the car.* **2.** In a direction opposite to: *against the rain.*

agree | ə **grē′** | v. To be in harmony with: *will agree with you.* **agrees, agreed, agreeing, agreeable, agreeably, agreeableness, agreement, agreements, agreeability**

agreement | ə **grē′** mənt | n. An understanding between people: *reached an agreement.* [see *agree*]

amend | ə **mĕnd′** | v. To change a bill, law, or motion by adding, omitting, or changing its wording: *to amend the law.* **amends, amended, amending, amendable, amendment, amendments, amender**

amendment | ə **mĕnd′**mənt | n. A change made in a law, bill, or motion by adding, omitting, or changing its wording: *an amendment to the rules.* [see *amend*]

amuse | ə **myōōz′** | v. To make smile or to entertain: *to amuse with toys and games.* **amuses, amused, amusing, amusable, amusement, amusements**

amusement | ə **myōōz′**mənt | n. Anything that entertains: *a brief, playful amusement.* **–Amusement park–**A park offering many forms of entertainment for profit. [see *amuse*]

anxious | **ăngk′**shəs | adj. Feeling uneasy or worried: *anxious thoughts.* **anxiously, anxiousness, anxiety, anxieties**

appeal | ə **pēl′** | n. An urgent request: *an appeal for food.* **appeals, appealed, appealing, appealingly, appealer**

appear | ə **pîr′** | v. To come into sight: *will soon appear.* **disappear, disappears, disappeared, disappearing, disappearance**

approve | ə **prōōv′** | v. To accept as satisfactory: *to approve the letter.* **approves, approved, approving, approvable, approval, approvals, approver**

area | **âr′**ē ə | n. A flat, open space: *a play area.* **areas**

argue | **är′gyōō** | v. To disagree: *will argue among themselves.* **argues, argued, arguing, argument, arguments, argumentative**

argument | **är′gy**ə mənt | n. A disagreement: *a foolish argument.* [see *argue*]

armor | **är′**mər | n. A metal or leather covering worn to protect the body in battle: *dressed in armor.* **armors, armored, armory**

arrange | ə **rānj′** | v. To put in order: *to arrange the new books.* **arranges, arranged, arranging, arranger, arrangement, arrangements**

arrangement | ə **rānj′**mənt | n. Something arranged in a certain way: *a colorful flower arrangement.* [see *arrange*]

arrest | ə **rĕst′** | n. A holding of a person by authority of the law: *the criminal's arrest.* **–Under arrest–**Held by the police. **arrests, arrested, arresting, arrester**

arrive | ə **rīv′** | v. To appear or come: *will arrive soon.* **arrives, arrived, arriving, arrival**

article | **är′tĭ** kəl | n. A written story, complete in itself, on a specific subject but included as part of a magazine, book, or newspaper: *an article on birds.* **articles**

assemble | ə **sĕm′**bəl | v. To call together or gather: *to assemble all the students.* **assembles, assembled, assembling, assemblage, assembly, assemblies, assembler**

assembly | ə **sĕm′**blē | n. A calling together of people for a special purpose; a meeting: *an assembly of lawyers.* [see *assemble*]

assign | ə **sīn′** | v. **1.** To give out: *to assign homework.* **2.** To appoint to: *to assign seats.* **assigns, assigned, assigning, assignable, assigner, assignment**

assigned | ə **sīnd′** | v. **1.** Gave out: *assigned tasks.* **2.** Appointed; placed: *assigned to the front row.* [see *assign*]

assist | ə **sĭst′** | v. To help; aid: *to assist the doctor.* **assists, assisted, assisting, assistant, assistance**

ă pat / ā pay / â care / ä father / ĕ pet / ē be / ĭ pit / ī pie / î fierce / ŏ pot / ō go / ô paw, for / oi oil / ŏŏ book /
ōō boot / ou out / ŭ cut / û fur / th the / th thin / hw which / zh vision / ə ago, item, pencil, atom, circus
©1977 by Houghton Mifflin Company. Reprinted by permission from THE AMERICAN HERITAGE SCHOOL DICTIONARY.

astonish | ə **stŏn′**ĭsh | v. To amaze or surprise: *will astonish the child.* **astonishes, astonished, astonishing, astonishingly, astonishment**

astonished | ə **stŏn′**ĭsht | adj. Amazed or surprised: *astonished crowd.* [see *astonish*]

athlete | **ăth′**lēt′ | n. A person trained in physical exercise: *a strong athlete.* **athletes, athletic, athletics**

attain | ə **tān′** | v. To achieve or reach by effort: *to attain greatness.* **attains, attained, attaining, attainable, attainment, attainer**

attend | ə **tĕnd′** | v. To give thought to: *to attend to the matter.* **attends, attended, attending, attentive, attentively, attentiveness, attendance, attendant, attention, attentions**

attention | ə **tĕn′**shən | n. **1.** Thought or focus: *attention to facts.* **2.** Mental concentration on someone or something: *to pay careful attention.* [see *attend*]

attract | ə **trăkt′** | v. To appeal to; be pleasing to: *will attract children.* **attracts, attracted, attracting, attractive, attractively, attractiveness, attraction**

attractive | ə **trăk′**tĭv | adj. Appealing or pleasing: *an attractive shirt.* [see *attract*]

auction | **ôk′**shən | n. A sale in which objects are sold to the person who offers the most money for them: *an auction of antiques.* **auctions, auctioned, auctioning, auctioneer**

author | **ô′**thər | n. A person who writes: *author of novels.* **authors, authored, authoring, authorial**

avoid | ə **void′** | v. To stay away from: *will avoid the ditch.* **avoids, avoided, avoiding, avoidable, avoidably, avoidance**

awful | **ô′**fəl | adj. Bad or frightening: *an awful accident.* **awfully, awfulness**

awfully | **ô′**fəl lē | adv. **1.** Badly: *drove awfully.* **2.** INFORMAL—Very much: *awfully active.* [see *awful*]

awkward | **ôk′**wərd | adj. Clumsy in movement: *an awkward little puppy.* **awkwardly, awkwardness**

B

balance | **băl′**əns | v. To put or hold in a steady position or condition: *to balance the weights.* n. A steady position or condition: *an even balance.* **balances, balanced, balancing, balancer**

bargain | **bâr′**gĭn | n. An agreement: *a fair bargain between us.* **bargains, bargained, bargaining, bargainer**

bathe | bā*th* | v. To wash: *will bathe the child.* **bathes, bathed, bathing, bath, bather**

battery | **băt′**ə rē | n. **1.** A single dry cell: *a light's battery.* **2.** A set of electric cells that supplies electric current: *a truck's battery.* **batteries**

behave | bĭ **hāv′** | v. To control oneself; act: *to behave like an adult.* **behaves, behaved, behaving, behavior, behavioral, behaviorally**

beneath | bĭ **nēth′** | prep. In a place below; under: *beneath the table.*

berry | **bĕr′** e | n. A small, fleshy fruit: *a wild berry.* **berries**

bicycle | **bī′** sĭk′əl | n. A metal vehicle with two wheels and a seat: *a red bicycle.* adj. Of or related to a bicycle: *a bicycle tire.* **bicycles, bicycled, bicycling, bicycler, bicyclist**

bluff | blŭf | n. Something done or said to fool others: *a difficult bluff.* **—Call one's bluff—**To ask for proof or to challenge someone's actions when trickery is suspected. **bluffs, bluffed, bluffing, bluffer**

boil | boil | v. To bubble and give off steam due to heating: *to boil the water.* **boils, boiled, boiling, boiler, boilers**

boiler | **boi′**lər | n. A storage tank for heating and holding hot water for a building: *a boiler in the basement.* [see *boil*]

borrow | **bŏr′**ō | v. To use or take something that must be returned: *will borrow the tools.* **borrows, borrowed, borrowing, borrower**

borrowed | **bŏr′** ōd | v. Used something, knowing it must be returned: *borrowed her book.* [see *borrow*]

breathe | brē*th* | v. To take air into the lungs and force it out: *to breathe easily.* **breathes, breathed, breathing, breathable, breather, breath**

brief | brēf | *adj.* Short; quick: *a brief speech.* ***briefs, briefed, briefing, briefness, briefer, briefest, briefly***

broad | brôd | *adj.* Wide across: *a broad sidewalk.* ***broader, broadest, broaden, broadens, broadened, broadening, broadly, broadness***

burden | bûr′dn | *n.* A load; something carried: *to drop the burden.* ***burdens, burdened, burdening, burdensome***

buried | bĕr′ēd | *v.* Hid or covered up: *has buried the bone.* [see *bury*]

bury | bĕr′ē | *v.* To hide or cover up: *to bury gold.* ***buries, buried, burying, burial, burier***

bushel | bŏosh′əl | *n.* A measure for dry goods that equals 4 pecks or 32 quarts: *picked a bushel.* ***bushels, busheled, busheling***

business | bĭz′nĭs | *n.* A factory, store, or other commercial establishment; a company: *a major business.* [see *busy*]

busy | bĭz′ē | *adj.* Full of activity: *a busy airport.* ***busier, busiest, busies, busied, busying, busyness, business, businesses***

C

cabinet | kăb′ə nĭt | *n.* A compartment or cupboard used for displaying or storing objects: *an empty cabinet.* ***cabinets***

calendar | kăl′ən dər | *n.* **1.** A list of dates in order of occurrence: *a monthly calendar.* **2.** A chart showing days and months of a particular year: *a wall calendar.* ***calendars***

campus | kăm′pəs | *n.* College or school grounds: *a peaceful campus.* ***campuses***

capable | kā′pə bəl | *adj.* Able: *two capable ice skaters.* ***capably, capableness, capability***

capital | kăp′ĭ tl | *n.* **1.** A city where the government of a state, province, or nation is located: *the state's capital.* **2.** Money or property used to increase one's wealth: *not enough capital.* —**Capital letter**—A letter used to begin a sentence or other important words, such as those in book titles. ***capitals, capitalize, capitalizes, capitalized, capitalizing, capitalization, capitalist***

capture | kăp′chər | *v.* To take a person or thing by force: *to capture the fort.* ***captures, captured, capturing, captive, captivity***

care | kâr | *n.* Caution: *moved with care.* ***cares, cared, caring, careful, carefully, carefulness***

carefully | kâr′fəl ē | *adv.* Cautiously: *placed carefully.* [see *care*]

catalog | kăt′l ôg′ | *n.* A book containing a list of items and a description of each: *a store catalog.* ***catalogs, cataloged, cataloging, cataloger***

caution | kô′shən | *n.* Much care: *looked with caution.* ***cautions, cautioned, cautioning, cautionary, cautious, cautiously, cautiousness***

cement | sĭ mĕnt′ | *adj.* Of or related to cement: *a cement sidewalk.* *n.* **1.** A substance used to make concrete and mortar: *paved with cement.* **2.** Anything soft which hardens and causes things to stick together: *a quick-drying cement.* ***cements, cemented, cementing, cementer***

century | sĕn′chə rē | *n.* **1.** Each 100 years starting from a particular time: *the seventeenth century.* **2.** One hundred years: *lived for a century.* ***centuries***

certain | sûr′tn | *adj.* Showing no doubt; sure: *is certain of these facts.* ***uncertain, uncertainly, uncertainty, uncertainness***

chalk | chôk | *n.* A soft substance made from fossil shells, used for writing on a chalkboard: *the teacher's chalk.* ***chalks, chalked, chalking, chalky***

chamber | chām′bər | *n.* A room: *asleep in her own chamber.* ***chambers, chambered, chambering***

ă pat / ā pay / â care / ä father / ĕ pet / ē be / ĭ pit / ī pie / î fierce / ŏ pot / ō go / ô paw, for / oi oil / ŏŏ book / ŏŏ boot / ou out / ŭ cut / û fur / *th* the / th thin / hw which / zh vision / ə ago, item, pencil, atom, circus
©1977 by Houghton Mifflin Company. Reprinted by permission from THE AMERICAN HERITAGE SCHOOL DICTIONARY.

champion | **chăm′**pē ən | *n.* The person, thing, or animal that wins a contest or game: *the local sixth-grade spelling champion.* **champions, championed, championing, championship**

channel | **chăn′**əl | *n.* **1.** A river or stream bed: *a river's channel.* **2.** An airwave of a radio or television station: *switched the channel.* **channels, channeled, channeling**

chapter | **chăp′**tər | *n.* A division in a book: *my favorite chapter.* **chapters**

charity | **chăr′**ĭ tē | *n.* A giving to the poor or to an organization that helps the poor, sick, or helpless: *clothes for charity.* **charities, charitable, charitably, charitableness**

charm | **chärm** | *n.* Appeal or power of pleasing: *has great charm.* **charms, charmed, charming, charmingly, charmer**

charming | **chär′**mĭng | *adj.* Very appealing: *a charming smile.* [see *charm*]

cheap | **chēp** | *adj.* Inexpensive; costing very little: *a cheap fare.* **cheaper, cheapest, cheapen, cheapens, cheapened, cheaply, cheapness**

citizen | **sĭt′**ĭ zən | *n.* **1.** A person who is a member of a nation by choice or by birth: *a U.S. citizen.* **2.** A member of a town or city: *a local citizen.* **citizens, citizenry, citizenship**

claim | **klām** | *v.* To ask for, insist, or demand as one's own: *to claim the title.* *n.* A demand or request: *made a claim.* **claims, claimed, claiming, claimable, claimant**

claims | **klāmz** | *v.* Demands, insists, or requests: *claims the box.* *n.* More than one claim: *several claims were received.* [see *claim*]

coarse | **kôrs** | *adj.* Rough in texture: *a coarse surface.* **coarser, coarsest, coarsen, coarsened, coarsely, coarseness**

collect | **kə lĕkt′** | *v.* **1.** To gather or accumulate: *will collect the dirt.* **2.** To bring together to make a set: *to collect old dolls.* **collects, collected, collecting, collectable, collector, collection**

colonies | **kŏl′**ə nēz | *n.* More than one group of plants or animals living or growing together: *insect colonies.* [see *colony*]

colony | **kŏl′**ə nē | *n.* **1.** A group of people living together and sharing the same background, occupation, or interest: *a colony of jazz musicians.* **2.** A group of the same kind of plants or animals that live or grow together: *a large ant colony.* **colonies, colonize, colonizes, colonized, colonizing, colonization, colonial, colonially, colonialism, colonist**

command | **kə mănd′** | *n.* A direction or order: *shouted a command.* *v.* To direct or order: *will command them to leave.* **commands, commanded, commanding, commander, commandment, commandments**

comment | **kŏm′**ĕnt′ | *v.* To make a remark: *will comment on the speech.* *n.* A brief statement or remark about something that has been written, said, or done: *had read the boss's comment.* **comments, commented, commenting, commentator**

common | **kŏm′**ən | *adj.* Ordinary; usual: *a common plant.* **commoner, commonest, commonly, commonness**

companion | **kəm păn′**yən | *n.* A person who associates with another; friend: *a childhood companion.* **companions, companionship, companionable**

complete | **kəm plēt′** | *v.* To finish: *to complete the homework.* **completes, completed, completing, completely, completeness, completion**

compute | **kəm pyo͞ot′** | *v.* To find solutions by mathematics or computers: *will compute the answer.* **computes, computed, computing, computerize, computer, computers**

computer | **kəm pyo͞o′**tər | *n.* An electronic machine that can store, process, and analyze data: *bought a new computer.* [see *compute*]

concern | **kən sûrn′** | *n.* Worry or anxiety: *a look of concern.* **concerns, concerned, concerning, concernment**

concerned | **kən sûrnd′** | *adj.* Troubled; worried: *a concerned mother.* [see *concern*]

concert | **kŏn′**sûrt′ | *n.* A musical performance which involves several musicians or singers: *a piano concert.* **concerts, concerto**

confuse | **kən fyo͞oz′** | *v.* To cause disorder; mix up: *might confuse the drivers.* **confuses, confused, confusing, confusingly, confusedly, confusion**

connect | kə **nĕkt′** | v. To join or link one thing to another: *will connect the wires.* **connects, connected, connecting, connective, connector, connection, connections**

connection | kə **nĕk′** shən | n. The act of linking one thing to another: *completed the connection.* —**In connection with**—In reference to. [see *connect*]

contain | kən **tān′** | v. To hold or have as contents: *does contain art supplies.* **contains, contained, containing, containable, container, containment**

contemplate | **kŏn′**təm plāt′ | v. To think about: *will contemplate the problem.* **contemplates, contemplated, contemplating**

continent | **kŏn′**tə nənt | n. One of the seven largest land masses on earth: *the continent of Asia.* **continents, continental**

continue | kən **tĭn′**yōō | v. To keep going: *will continue to walk.* **continues, continued, continuing, continuous, continuously, continual, continually, continuation, discontinue, discontinues, discontinued, discontinuing**

contribute | kən **trĭb′**yōot | v. To give: *will contribute ten dollars.* **contributes, contributed, contributing, contributor, contribution**

convention | kən **vĕn′**shən | n. A meeting arranged for a special purpose: *a sales convention.* **conventions**

convince | kən **vĭns′** | v. To cause to believe; persuade: *to convince them of the truth.* **convinces, convinced, convincing, convincingly**

cooperate | kō **ŏp′**ə răt′ | v. To work or act together with others: *will cooperate with him.* **cooperates, cooperated, cooperating, cooperative, cooperatively, cooperator, cooperativeness, cooperation**

countries | **kŭn′**trēz | n. More than one country: *war between two Asian countries.* [see *country*]

country | **kŭn′**trē | n. A nation: *a new country.* **countries**

courage | **kûr′**ĭj | n. Bravery: *a medal for courage.* **courageous, courageously**

creature | **krē′**chər | n. **1.** Something created: *a make-believe creature.* **2.** A living person or animal: *a lonely creature.* **creatures**

credit | **krĕd′**ĭt | n. Reputation or honor: *to one's credit.* v. To charge an amount, which will be paid at a later time: *will credit the sale.* **credits, credited, crediting**

creep | krēp | v. To move slowly; crawl: *to creep past the door.* **creeps, crept, creeping, creepy, creepier, creepiest, creepily, creepiness, creeper**

cruel | **krōō′**əl | adj. Causing pain: *a cruel act.* **crueler, cruelest, cruelly, cruelty, cruelness**

cultivate | **kŭl′**tə vāt′ | v. To grow: *will cultivate the corn crop.* **cultivates, cultivated, cultivating, cultivation, cultivator**

cunning | **kŭn′**ĭng | n. Slyness or cleverness: *showed much cunning.* adj. Sly or clever: *cunning animal.* **cunningly, cunningness**

curious | **kyŏor′**ē əs | adj. Eager to know something: *a curious student.* **curiously, curiosity, curiousness**

curtain | **kûr′**tn | n. Cloth hung at windows: *pulled back the white curtain.* **curtains, curtained**

curve | kûrv | n. **1.** A bend: *a curve in the driveway.* **2.** A line without a straight part; arc: *to draw a curve.* **curves, curved, curving**

cushion | **kōōsh′**ən | n. A soft pad or pillow: *a thick cushion.* **cushions, cushioned, cushioning**

customer | **kŭs′**tə mər | n. A person who purchases something: *a satisfied customer.* **customers**

ă pat / ā pay / â care / ä father / ĕ pet / ē be / ĭ pit / ī pie / î fierce / ŏ pot / ō go / ô paw, for / oi oil / ōo book /
ōō boot / ou out / ŭ cut / û fur / *th* the / th thin / hw which / zh vision / ə ago, item, pencil, atom, circus
©1977 by Houghton Mifflin Company. Reprinted by permission from THE AMERICAN HERITAGE SCHOOL DICTIONARY.

D

damage | **dăm'ĭj** | *n.* Injury that decreases value or usefulness: *damage from the flood.* *v.* To cause injury so as to decrease value or usefulness: *might damage the spare tire.* *damages, damaged, damaging, damageable*

danger | **dān'jər** | *n.* The chance or risk of harm: *close to danger.* *dangers, dangerous, dangerously*

dangerous | **dān'jər əs** | *adj.* Likely to be harmful: *a dangerous voyage.* [see *danger*]

debate | **dĭ bāt'** | *n.* An argument that gives reasons for and against: *a loud debate* *v.* To discuss reasons for and against: *to debate a topic.* *debates, debated, debating, debatable*

debt | **dĕt** | *n.* **1.** The condition of owing someone: *one hundred dollars in debt.* **2.** Something owed: *a large debt.* *debts, debtor*

decent | **dē'sənt** | *adj.* Proper: *a decent life.* *decently, decency*

declare | **dĭ klâr'** | *v.* To state publicly or formally: *to declare peace.* *declares, declared, declaring, declarative, declaredly, declarer, declaration*

decline | **dĭ klīn'** | *v.* To refuse politely: *to decline to go.* *declines, declined, declining, declinable, decliner*

decorate | **dĕk'ə rāt'** | *v.* **1.** To paint, paper, furnish, etc., a room: *will decorate the kitchen.* **2.** To make pretty: *will decorate the cake.* *decorates, decorated, decorating, decorative, decorativeness, decoration, decorator*

defeat | **dĭ fēt'** | *n.* A loss: *an unexpected defeat.* *defeats, defeated, defeating, defeatist, defeater*

defend | **dĭ fĕnd'** | *v.* To protect: *will defend the village.* *defends, defended, defending, defense, defenses, defensive, defensively, defensiveness, defenseless, defender, defendant*

defense | **dĭ fĕns'** | *n.* A protection against harm or attack: *defense of the harbor.* [see *defend*]

delight | **dĭ līt'** | *n.* Great joy: *his delight over the gift.* *delights, delighted, delighting, delightedly, delightful, delightfully, delightfulness*

delightfully | **dĭ līt'fəl ē** | *adv.* Very pleasantly: *laughed delightfully.* [see *delight*]

deliver | **dĭ lĭv'ər** | *v.* To carry and distribute: *will deliver the packages.* *delivers, delivered, delivering, delivery, deliveries, deliverer*

delivery | **dĭ lĭv'ə rē** | *adj.* Of or related to a delivery: *delivery service.* *n.* **1.** A carrying and distributing of goods: *made a delivery.* **2.** Something that is delivered: *paid for the delivery.* [see *deliver*]

dentist | **dĕn'tĭst** | *n.* A doctor who takes care of teeth: *a visit to the dentist.* *dentists, dental, dentally, dentistry*

department | **dĭ pärt'mənt** | *n.* A division or part of some whole: *the shoe department.* *departments, departmental, departmentally*

deposit | **dĭ pŏz'ĭt** | *n.* Money put into a bank account: *mailed the deposit.* *v.* To put down: *to deposit his clothes.* *deposits, deposited, depositing, depositor*

depth | **dĕpth** | *n.* The distance from top to bottom: *the hole's depth.* *depths*

deserve | **dĭ zûrv'** | *v.* To have a right to: *to deserve more credit.* *deserves, deserved, deserving, deservedly*

design | **dĭ zīn'** | *n.* A sketch of how something will be made: *a design of the house.* *v.* To draw plans for how something is to be made: *to design a new computer.* *designs, designed, designing, designer*

desire | **dĭ zīr'** | *v.* To want or long for: *to desire some water.* *desires, desired, desiring, desirous, desirously, desirable, desirably*

dessert | **dĭ zûrt'** | *n.* The last course of a meal, often a pastry, fruit, or ice cream: *a sweet dessert.* *desserts*

destroy | **dĭ stroi'** | *v.* To break into pieces or make useless: *will destroy the building.* *destroys, destroyed, destroying, destroyer, destructive, destruction*

diameter | **dī ăm'ĭt ər** | *n.* The straight line that passes through the center of a circle or sphere: *measured the diameter.* *diameters*

diamond | **dī'mənd** | *n.* A precious stone formed of pure carbon in crystals: *bought a diamond.* *diamonds*

dictionary | **dĭk'shə nĕr'ē** | *n.* A book that gives information about words, which are arranged in alphabetical order: *the student's dictionary.* *dictionaries*

diet | **dī′ĭt** | *n.* A special selection of foods eaten because of illness or in order to lose or gain weight: *a meatless diet.* **diets, dieted, dieting, dietary, dietetic, dieter, dietician**

differ | **dĭf′ər** | *v* **1.** To be unalike: *to differ in age.* **2.** To disagree: *to differ on issues.* **differs, differed, differing, different, differently**

difficult | **dĭf′ĭ kŭlt′** | *adj.* Hard to do: *a difficult test.* **difficultly, difficulty, difficulties**

direct | **dĭ rĕkt′** | *v.* **1.** To tell or show: *as I direct you.* **2.** To lead: *will direct the choir.* **directs, directed, directing, directly, direction, directions, directional, directness, director, directory, directorship**

directed | **dĭ rĕk′tĭd** | *v.* **1.** Told or shown: *directed them to their seats.* **2.** Led: *directed the band.* [see *direct*]

direction | **dĭ rĕk′shən** | *n.* **1.** The way in which someone or something faces or points: *in the car's direction.* **2.** An instruction or command: *a simple direction.* [see *direct*]

disappear | **dĭs′ə pîr′** | *v.* To vanish or pass from sight: *to disappear in the dark.* [see *appear*]

disaster | **dĭ zăs′tər** | *n.* A great misfortune that causes much suffering or loss: *a horrible train disaster.* **disasters, disastrous, disastrously**

discontinue | **dĭs′kən tĭn′yōō** | *v.* To end: *will discontinue the game.* [see *continue*]

discuss | **dĭ skŭs′** | *v.* To talk over: *will discuss the problem.* **discusses, discussed, discussing, discussable, discusser, discussion**

disease | **dĭ zēz′** | *n.* An illness or infection: *disease of the skin.* **diseases, diseased**

dislike | **dĭs līk′** | *n.* A feeling of not liking: *a dislike of apples. v.* To care little for: *to dislike sports.* [see *like*]

dismiss | **dĭs mĭs′** | *v.* To send away or excuse: *will dismiss the army troops.* **dismisses, dismissed, dismissing, dismissal**

dispute | **dĭ spyōōt′** | *n.* An argument or debate: *a loud dispute.* **disputes, disputed, disputing, disputable**

distant | **dĭs′tənt** | *adj.* Faraway: *a distant land.* **distantly, distance**

district | **dĭs′trĭkt** | *n.* An area or region: *a farming district.* **districts**

disturb | **dĭ stûrb′** | *v.* **1.** To destroy the peace of: *to disturb the quiet.* **2.** To bother or annoy: *to disturb with silly questions.* **disturbs, disturbed, disturbing, disturbingly, disturber, disturbance**

divide | **dĭ vīd′** | *v.* **1.** To perform the mathematical operation of separating a number into equal parts: *to divide 100 by 50.* **2.** To split or separate: *to divide the bread.* **divides, divided, dividing, divisible, divider, dividend, division, divisions**

division | **dĭ vĭzh′ən** | *n.* **1.** The mathematical operation of dividing one number by another number: *to learn division.* **2.** A part or section: *a division of the company.* **3.** Something that keeps separate: *a glass division.* [see *divide*]

document | **dŏk′yə mənt** | *n.* An official paper that gives information or proof of some fact: *filed a document for the court case.* **documents, documented, documenting, documentation, documentary**

doubt | **dout** | *v.* To be unsure; question: *doesn't doubt his guilt.* **—Without doubt—**Surely or certainly. **doubts, doubted, doubting, doubtingly, doubtable, doubtful, doubtfully, doubtfulness, doubtless, doubtlessly, doubtlessness, doubter**

E

eager | **ē′gər** | *adj.* Full of impatient curiosity: *an eager learner.* **eagerly, eagerness**

easy | **ē′zē** | *adj.* Relaxed; comfortable: *an easy manner.* **uneasy, uneasier, uneasiest, uneasily, uneasiness**

echo | **ĕk′ō** | *n.* A repeating of a sound: *his voice's echo.* **echoes, echoed, echoing**

effort | **ĕf′ərt** | *n.* A strong attempt: *an effort to finish.* **efforts, effortless, effortlessly**

ă pat / ā pay / â care / ä father / ĕ pet / ē be / ĭ pit / ī pie / î fierce / ŏ pot / ō go / ô paw, for / oi oil / ŏŏ book / ōō boot / ou out / ŭ cut / û fur / *th* the / th thin / hw which / zh vision / ə ago, item, pencil, atom, circus
©1977 by Houghton Mifflin Company. Reprinted by permission from THE AMERICAN HERITAGE SCHOOL DICTIONARY.

elect | ĭ **lĕkt′** | v. To choose for an office by voting: *will elect a president this week.* **elects, elected, electing, elective, electively, elector, electoral, electorate, election, elections, electioneer**

election | ĭ **lĕk′**shən | n. A choosing for an office by vote: *an election for governor.* [see *elect*]

element | **ĕl′**ə mənt | n. 1. An important feature: *a necessary element.* 2. A substance that cannot be broken down chemically: *tested the element.* **elements**

elevate | **ĕl′**ə vāt′ | v. To raise or lift upward: *will elevate the seat.* **elevates, elevated, elevating, elevation, elevator, elevators**

elevator | **ĕl′**ə vā′tər | n. A platform or cage used to move people or things from one floor to another of a building: *a full elevator.* [see *elevate*]

empire | **ĕm′**pīr′ | n. A group of states or nations under one ruler: *a powerful empire.* **empires, emperor, empress**

enemies | **ĕn′**ə mēz | n. More than one enemy: *many angry enemies.* [see *enemy*]

enemy | **ĕn′**ə mē | n. A person or group of persons that hate and try to hurt each other: *an evil enemy.* **enemies**

energy | **ĕn′**ər jē | n. Power or fuel for making things work: *solar energy.* **energies, energetic, energetically, energize, energizes, energized, energizing, energizer**

enforce | ĕn **fôrs′** | v. To force obedience to: *will enforce the rules.* **enforces, enforced, enforcing, enforceable, enforcer, enforcement**

entertain | ĕn′tər **tān′** | v. To amuse or please: *will entertain the guests.* **entertains, entertained, entertaining, entertainer, entertainingly, entertainment**

entire | ĕn **tīr′** | adj. Whole or complete: *the entire pie.* **entirely, entirety, entireness**

entirely | ĕn **tīr′**lē | adv. Completely: *entirely pleased.* [see *entire*]

envelope | **ĕn′**və lōp′ | n. A paper cover with a gummed flap in which a letter or anything flat can be mailed: *an airmail envelope.* **envelopes**

equal | **ē′**kwəl | adj. The same; even: *equal amounts of flour and water.* **equals, equaled, equaling, equally, equalize, equality, equalizer**

error | **ĕr′**ər | n. A mistake: *an error in arithmetic.* **errors, errorless**

establish | ĭ **stăb′**lĭsh | v. 1. To set up on a lasting basis; found: *will establish a territory.* 2. To arrange or set up: *to establish a law practice.* **establishes, established, establishing, establishment**

estate | ĭ **stāt′** | n. 1. A large piece of property belonging to someone: *a magnificent estate.* 2. The objects and property left by a dead person: *left her estate to her children.* **estates**

evil | **ē′**vəl | adj. Wicked: *evil thoughts.* **eviler, evilest, evilly, evils, evilness**

exact | ĭg **zăkt′** | adj. Correct or accurate; precise: *exact answer.* **exactly, exactness**

exactly | ĭg **zăkt′**lē | adv. Correctly or precisely: *measured exactly.* [see *exact*]

example | ĭg **zăm′**pəl | n. A pattern or model to be imitated: *shown as an example.* **examples**

exchange | ĭks **chānj′** | v. To change or trade for another: *may exchange the blouse.* **exchanges, exchanged, exchanging, exchangeable, exchanger**

excite | ĭk **sīt′** | v. To stir up the emotions of: *will excite the crowd.* **excites, excited, exciting, excitingly, excitedly, excitable, excitably, exciter, excitement**

excitement | ĭk **sīt′**mənt | n. Enthusiasm: *excitement over the race.* [see *excite*]

exclaim | ĭk **sklām′** | v. To speak suddenly or cry out: *to exclaim with surprise.* **exclaims, exclaimed, exclaiming, exclamatory, exclaimer, exclamation**

exercise | **ĕk′**sər sīz′ | n. An activity requiring physical exertion to maintain or create fitness: *walked for exercise.* **exercises, exercised, exercising, exerciser**

exhibit | ĭg **zĭb′**ĭt | n. A display or show: *a science exhibit.* v. To show or display: *will exhibit the project.* **exhibits, exhibited, exhibiting, exhibition, exhibitor**

expect | ĭk **spĕkt′** | v. To look forward to or think something will happen: *to expect a phone call.* **expects, expected, expecting, expectable, expectant, expectantly, expectedly, expectancy, expectation**

expense | ĭk **spĕns′** | n. The cost or the amount of money spent: *expense of the coat.* **expenses, expensive, expensively, expensiveness**

expensive | ĭk **spĕn′** sĭv | *adj.* Costly: *a very expensive ring.* [see *expense*]

expert | **ĕk′**spûrt′ | *adj.* Having great skill, experience, or knowledge in a particular subject: *an expert mechanic. n.* A person who has great knowledge about a subject: *an expert on animals.* **experts, expertly, expertness**

explain | ĭk **splān′** | *v.* To make clear or understandable: *will explain the riddle of the missing doll.* **explains, explained, explaining, explainable, explanatory, explanation**

explore | ĭk **splôr′** | *v.* To travel or wander through an unfamiliar place: *to explore the cove.* **explores, explored, exploring, exploratory, explorer, exploration**

expose | ĭk **spōz′** | *v.* To uncover or lay open: *to expose to air.* **exposes, exposed, exposing, exposure, exposer, exposition**

express | ĭk **sprĕs′** | *n.* A train, bus, etc., that travels fast and makes few stops: *took an express. v.* To show by look, voice, or action: *to express sadness.* **expresses, expressed, expressing, expressive, expressiveness, expressively, expression, expressions, expressionless**

extent | ĭk **stĕnt′** | *n.* **1.** The range of something: *the extent of the damage.* **2.** The distance or area to which a thing extends: *the extent of the property.* **extends, extend, extends, extended, extending, extensive, extension, extender**

extra | **ĕk′**strə | *adj.* Additional: *an extra layer.* **extras**

F

factories | **făk′**tə rēz | *n.* More than one factory: *the automobile factories.* [see *factory*]

factory | **făk′**tə rē | *n.* A building where goods are made: *a busy factory.* **factories**

familiar | fə **mĭl′**yər | *adj.* Well-known or common: *a familiar book.* **familiarly, familiarize, familiarizes, familiarized, familiarizing, familiarity, familiarities**

farewell | fâr′**wĕl′** | *n.* The act of saying good-by: *waved a farewell.* **farewells**

fault | fôlt | *n.* **1.** Responsibility for an error: *the fault of the owner.* **2.** A defect or flaw: *its worst fault.* **faults, faulted, faulting, faulty, faultless, faultlessly, faultiness**

favor | **fā′**vər | *v.* **1.** To help or benefit: *would favor their needs.* **2.** To like or prefer: *to favor her idea.* **favors, favored, favoring, favorable, favorably, favorableness, favorite, favorites, favoritism**

favorable | **fā′**vər ə bəl | *adj.* Positive or pleasing: *a favorable decision.* [see *favor*]

favorite | **fā′**vər ĭt | *adj.* Liked best; preferred: *my favorite movie.* [see *favor*]

figure | **fig′**yər | *n.* **1.** A shape or form: *a dark figure.* **2.** A symbol for a number: *the figure 10.* —**Figure out**—To understand. **figures, figured, figuring, figurine**

final | **fī′**nəl | *adj.* Allowing no further actions: *his final word.* **finals, finally, finalize, finalizes, finalized, finalizing, finalist, finale**

finally | **fī′**nə lē | *adv.* At last: *has finally finished.* [see *final*]

firm | fûrm | *adj.* **1.** Strong and sure: *a firm hold.* **2.** Steady; unshaking: *a firm belief.* **firms, firmed, firming, firmer, firmest, firmly, firmness**

flavor | **flā′**vər | *n.* Taste: *a strawberry flavor. v.* To give a taste to: *will flavor the meat.* **flavors, flavored, flavoring, flavorful, flavorfully, flavorsome, flavorless, flavorlessly**

forbid | fər **bĭd′** | *v.* Not to allow: *will forbid them to leave.* **forbids, forbade, forbidden, forbidding, forbiddingly, forbiddance**

forbidden | fər **bĭd′**n | *adj.* Not allowed: *a forbidden food.* [see *forbid*]

force | fôrs | *n.* Strength or power: *the force of the explosion.* **forces, forced, forcing, forcible, forcibly, forceful, forcefully, forcefulness**

forehead | **fôr′**hĕd′ | *n.* The upper part of the face above the eyes: *hit his forehead.* **foreheads**

ă pat / ā pay / â care / ä father / ĕ pet / ē be / ĭ pit / ī pie / î fierce / ŏ pot / ō go / ô paw, for / oi oil / o͞o book / o͞o boot / ou out / ŭ cut / û fur / *th* the / th thin / hw which / zh vision / ə ago, item, pencil, atom, circus
©1977 by Houghton Mifflin Company. Reprinted by permission from THE AMERICAN HERITAGE SCHOOL DICTIONARY.

foreign | **fôr′ĭn** | *adj.* **1.** Of or from another country: *foreign food.* **2.** Not belonging or related: *found a foreign object.* **foreigner, foreigners, foreignness**

fortune | **fôr′chən** | *n.* Great wealth: *won a fortune.* **–Fortune cookie–**An Oriental cookie which has a saying or a prediction of a fortune written on a piece of paper inside. **fortunes, fortunate, fortunately, fortuneless**

frank | **frăngk** | *adj.* Free and open about expressing one's thoughts: *a frank opinion.* **franker, frankest, frankly, frankness**

frankly | **frăngk′lē** | *adv.* In an open manner: *expressed frankly.* [see *frank*]

freight | **frāt** | *n.* Goods carried by a vessel or vehicle; cargo: *the ship's freight.* **freighter**

fright | **frīt** | *n.* Sudden terror: *a look of fright.* **frights, frighten, frightens, frightened, frightening, frighteningly, frightful, frightfully**

frighten | **frīt′n** | *v.* To fill with fear: *might frighten the crowd.* [see *fright*]

full | **fōol** | *adj.* Unable to hold anymore; filled: *a full glass.* **fuller, fullest, fully, fullness**

fully | **fōol′ē** | *adv.* Completely: *fully cooked.* [see *full*]

funeral | **fyōo′nər əl** | *adj.* Of or related to a funeral: *a funeral director. n.* The services accompanying the burial or burning of a dead person's body: *a quiet funeral.* **funerals**

furnace | **fûr′nĭs** | *n.* An enclosed box in which an intense fire is created to heat buildings or melt metals: *the house's furnace.* **furnaces**

furnish | **fûr′nĭsh** | *v.* To supply with furniture or equipment: *will furnish the apartment.* **furnishes, furnished, furnishing, furnishings, furnisher, furniture**

furniture | **fûr′nə chər** | *n.* Movable articles such as chairs, tables, etc., which make an area fit for living or working: *arranged the furniture.* [see *furnish*]

future | **fyōo′chər** | *n.* The time that is to come: *planned for the future. adj.* Of or related to the future: *a future meeting.* **futures, futuristic**

G

gallop | **găl′əp** | *v.* To go very fast: *to gallop away.* **gallops, galloped, galloping, galloper**

garbage | **gär′bĭj** | *adj.* Of or related to garbage: *a garbage bag. n.* Anything worthless: *put into the garbage.*

gear | **gîr** | *n.* **1.** A set of toothed wheels that fit together and often move at different speeds to transmit power: *switched the gear.* **2.** Equipment: *packed her hiking gear.* **gears, geared, gearing**

gentle | **jĕn′tl** | *adj.* Not violent or rough; mild: *a gentle manner.* **gentler, gentlest, gently, gentleness**

ghost | **gōst** | *n.* A dead person's spirit, believed by some to exist: *a ghost in the haunted house.* **ghosts, ghostly**

glance | **glăns** | *n.* A brief look: *a shy glance. v.* To look briefly: *glance suddenly away.* **glances, glanced, glancing**

glitter | **glĭt′ər** | *n.* A sparkling brightness: *the glitter of the water. v.* To sparkle or shine: *will glitter in the light.* **glitters, glittered, glittering, glitteringly, glittery**

gloom | **glōom** | *n.* Darkness; dimness: *full of gloom.* **gloomy, gloomier, gloomiest, gloomily, gloominess**

gloomy | **glōo′mē** | *adj.* Dark and dreary: *gloomy weather.* [see *gloom*]

glory | **glôr′ē** | *n.* Fame or honor: *tale of the hero's glory.* **glories, glorify, glorifies, glorified, glorifying, glorifier, glorious, gloriously**

gossip | **gŏs′əp** | *n.* Idle rumors: *a neighbor's gossip.* **gossips, gossiped, gossiping, gossipy, gossiper**

govern | **gŭv′ərn** | *v.* To direct or rule with authority: *to govern the territory.* **governs, governed, governing, governable, governor, government, governments**

government | **gŭv′ərn mənt** | *adj.* Of or related to a government: *a government agency. n.* The ruling system of a country, state, district, etc.: *a democratic government.* [see *govern*]

grateful | **grāt′fəl** | *adj.* Thankful: *grateful for the gift.* **gratefully, gratefulness**

great | **grāt** | *adj.* Large: *a great animal.* **greater, greatest, greatly, greatness**

greater | **grā′**tər | *adj.* Larger: *a greater amount.* [see *great*]

grief | grēf | *n.* Extreme sadness: *tears of grief.* *grieve, grieves, grieved, grieving, grievous, grievance*

groceries | **grō′**sə rēz | *n.* Articles of food and supplies sold by a grocer: *delivered the groceries.* [see *grocery*]

grocery | **grō′**sə rē | *n.* A store selling food and household items: *fruit from the grocery.* *groceries, grocer*

H

handkerchief | **hăng′**kər chĭf | *n.* A small square cloth used to wipe the nose, brow, etc.: *folded the handkerchief.* *handkerchiefs*

happiness | **hăp′**ē nĭs | *n.* Gladness: *shouted with happiness.* [see *happy*]

happy | **hăp′**ē | *adj.* Pleased or glad: *a happy laugh.* *happier, happiest, happily, happiness*

harmony | **här′**mə nē | *n.* **1.** Agreement in feeling; good will: *lived in harmony.* **2.** A blending together of musical sounds: *to sing in harmony.* *harmonize, harmonizes, harmonized, harmonizing, harmonizer, harmonies, harmonious, harmoniously, harmoniousness, harmonics, harmonist*

haste | hāst | *n.* Hurry: *made in haste.* *hasten, hastens, hastened, hastening, hasty, hastily*

headache | **hĕd′**āk′ | *n.* A pain occurring in the head: *sick with a headache.* *headaches*

health | hĕlth | *n.* The condition of the body or mind: *in perfect health.* *healthy, healthier, healthiest, healthful, healthfully, healthily, healthiness, healthfulness*

healthy | **hĕl′**thē | *adj.* Producing or giving health: *a healthy diet.* [see *health*]

height | hīt | *n.* The measurement from top to bottom of a thing or person: *the man's height.* *heights, heighten, heightens, heightened, heightening*

hesitate | **hĕz′**ĭ tāt′ | *v.* To pause or hold back: *to hesitate at the door.* *hesitates, hesitated, hesitating, hesitatingly, hesitant, hesitater, hesitation*

high | hī | *adj.* Greater than others: *at a high cost.* *higher, highest, highly, highness*

highly | **hī′**lē | *adv.* Very much or in an extreme degree: *highly intelligent.* [see *high*]

horizon | hə **rī′**zən | *n.* The line where the earth and sky appear to meet: *colorful sunset on the horizon.* *horizons, horizontal, horizontally*

human | **hyōō′**mən | *n.* A person: *footprints of a human.* *adj.* Of or relating to people: *human error.* *humans, humanly, humane, humanely, humanitarian, humanity, humanness, humanist, humanism*

humor | **hyōō′**mər | *n.* A funny or entertaining quality: *a joke with good humor.* *humors, humored, humoring, humorous, humorously, humorist*

I

idle | **īd′**l | *adj.* Not busy: *an idle worker.* *idles, idled, idling, idly, idleness, idler*

import | **ĭm′**pôrt′ | *adj.* Of or related to an import: *an import charge.* *v.* To bring in goods from another country for trade or sale: *to import silk.* *imports, imported, importing, importable, importer, importation*

important | ĭm **pôr′**tnt | *adj.* Valuable or necessary: *an important package in the mail.* *importantly, importance*

impossible | ĭm **pôs′**ə bəl | *adj.* Not able to be done: *an impossible task.* [see *possible*]

improve | ĭm **prōōv′** | *v.* To make better: *will improve the recipe.* *improves, improved, improving, improvable, improvement, improvements*

improvement | ĭm **prōōv′**mənt | *n.* A change or addition for the better: *improvement of the neighborhood.* [see *improve*]

impulse | **ĭm′**pŭls′ | *n.* A sudden urge: *an impulse to leave for home.* *impulses, impulsive, impulsively*

ă pat / ā pay / â care / ä father / ĕ pet / ē be / ĭ pit / ī pie / î fierce / ŏ pot / ō go / ô paw, for / oi oil / ŏŏ book / ōō boot / ou out / ŭ cut / û fur / *th* the / th thin / hw which / zh vision / ə ago, item, pencil, atom, circus
©1977 by Houghton Mifflin Company. Reprinted by permission from THE AMERICAN HERITAGE SCHOOL DICTIONARY.

incline | ĭn **klĭn'** | v. To have a tendency; tend: *incline to eat too fast.* **inclines, inclined, inclining, inclination**

inclined | ĭn **klīnd'** | adj. Willing; tending: *was inclined to leave.* [see *incline*]

include | ĭn **klo̅o̅d'** | v. To be part of a total amount: *does include the tip.* **includes, included, including, inclusive, inclusion**

income | **ĭn'kŭm'** | n. The money made from employment, business, property, etc.: *earns a good income.* **incomes, incoming**

increase | **ĭn'krēs** | n. A gain in amount or size: *a rapid increase in weight.* **increases, increased, increasing, increasingly**

independent | ĭn'dĭ **pĕn'**dənt | adj. Not depending on others: *began an independent activity.* **independently, independence, independency**

infant | **ĭn'**fənt | n. A baby or very young child: *carried the infant home.* **infants, infantile, infancy**

injure | **ĭn'**jər | v. To harm: *to injure an arm.* **injures, injured, injuring, injurious, injurer, injury, injuries**

inning | **ĭn'**ĭng | n. A division in a baseball game, with a top and a bottom half during which each team has a turn at bat: *the second inning.* **innings**

inquire | ĭn **kwīr'** | v. To ask about something: *may inquire about the sale.* **inquires, inquired, inquiring, inquiringly, inquiry, inquiries, inquirer, inquisition**

insect | **ĭn'** sĕkt' | n. One of a large group of small animals without a backbone. It has six legs and a body made up of three main divisions: *insect with wings.* **insects**

insects | **ĭn'**sĕkts' | n. More than one insect: *insects in the garden.* [see *insect*]

insist | ĭn **sĭst'** | v. To state strongly; demand: *to insist they go.* **insists, insisted, insisting, insistent, insistently**

inspect | ĭn **spĕkt'** | v. To examine carefully: *will inspect the room.* **inspects, inspected, inspecting, inspection, inspections, inspector**

inspection | ĭn **spĕk'**shən | n. An examination or close look: *an official inspection.* [see *inspect*]

instant | **ĭn'**stənt | n. A particular moment: *will start at this instant.* **instants, instantly, instantaneous, instantaneously, instance**

instead | ĭn **stĕd'** | adv. As a substitute: *had milk instead.* —**Instead of**—Rather than.

instruct | ĭn **strŭkt'** | v. To teach or train: *will instruct the science students.* **instructs, instructed, instructing, instruction, instructions, instructional, instructive, instructor**

instruction | ĭn **strŭk'**shən | n. A lesson or teaching: *skiing instruction.* [see *instruct*]

insure | ĭn **sho̅o̅r'** | v. 1. To buy insurance for something: *will insure the boat.* 2. To guarantee: *to insure good credit.* **insurers, insured, insuring, insurable, insurer, insurance**

introduce | ĭn'trə **do̅o̅s'** | v. 1. To present someone by name to another or others: *will introduce the new neighbor.* 2. To make known: *to introduce two new products to the public.* **introduces, introduced, introducing, introductory, introduction**

invent | ĭn **vĕnt'** | v. To think up and create something new: *to invent a new machine.* **invents, invented, inventing, inventive, inventively, inventiveness, invention, inventions, inventional, inventor**

invention | ĭn **vĕn'**shən | n. Something created, or invented, which did not exist before: *a scientific invention.* [see *invent*]

invitation | ĭn'vĭ **tā'**shən | n. A polite request to come somewhere: *an invitation to visit.* [see *invite*]

invite | ĭn **vīt'** | v. To ask someone politely to come somewhere: *will invite them to dinner.* **invites, invited, inviting, invitation, invitations**

issue | **ĭsh'**o̅o̅ | n. A certain quantity of magazines, newspapers, stamps, etc., sent out or given out at one time: *this month's issue.* v. To put out or send forth: *will issue a new set of rules.* **issues, issued, issuing, issuable**

J

jealous | **jĕl'**əs | adj. Full of envy: *a jealous act.* **jealously, jealousy, jealousness**

jewel | **jo̅o̅'**əl | n. A gem or precious stone: *a valuable jewel.* **jewels, jeweled, jeweling, jewelry, jeweler**

jewels | jo͞o′əlz | *n.* Precious stones: *sparkling like jewels.* [see *jewel*]

joint | joint | *n.* **1.** A place where two parts are connected: *a chair's joint.* **2.** The part of an animal or human where two bones join: *an ankle joint.* **joints, jointed, jointly**

journey | jûr′nē | *n.* A trip: *a long journey. v.* To take a trip; travel: *will journey west by bus.* **journeys, journeyed, journeying, journeyer**

jury | jo͞or′ē | *n.* A group of people chosen to give a judgment about something or someone: *a member of a jury.* **juries, juror**

just | jŭst | *adj.* Fair or honest: *a just law.* **unjust, unjustly, unjustness**

K

knit | nĭt | *v.* To make cloth or clothing by looping yarn or thread together by hand with long needles, or by machine: *to knit a sweater. adj.* Of a fabric made by knitting: *a knit suit.* **knits, knitted, knitting, knitter**

knitting | nĭt′ĭng | *v.* Making cloth by looping yarn or thread together: *is knitting a scarf. adj.* Of or related to knitting: *knitting instructions. n.* The process of making cloth from knitting: *learned knitting in school.* [see *knit*]

knowledge | nŏl′ ĭj | *n.* Understanding gained through experience or study: *knowledge of ancient cultures.* **knowledgeable**

L

labor | lā′bər | *n.* Work or toil: *proud of their labor.* —**Labor union**—An organization of workers united together to protect their interests. **labors, labored, laboring, laborious, laboriously, laborer**

landlord | lănd′lôrd′ | *n.* A person who owns land or buildings to rent to others: *met the landlord.* **landlords**

landscape | lănd′skāp′ | *n.* Scene; view: *a breathtaking landscape.* **landscapes, landscaping, landscaper**

lantern | lăn′tərn | *n.* A container for holding a light that shines through: *carried a lantern.* **lanterns**

last | lăst | *v.* To continue to exist: *will last for many years.* **lasts, lasted, lasting, lastingly, lastly, lastingness**

lasting | lăs′tĭng | *adj.* Remaining for a long time: *a lasting illness.* [see *last*]

launch | lônch | *v.* To set something in motion: *will launch the satellite.* **launches, launched, launching, launcher**

laundry | lôn′drē | *n.* Clothes, towels, etc., that are washed or need to be washed: *did the laundry.* **laundries, launder, launders, laundered, laundering, launderer, laundromat**

lawyer | lô′yər | *n.* A person trained to give legal advice and to represent clients in court: *hired a lawyer.* **lawyers**

lawyers | lô′yərz | *n.* More than one lawyer: *a meeting of lawyers.* [see *lawyer*]

league | lēg | *adj.* Of a league: *a league player. n.* An association of sports teams or clubs: *a baseball league.* **leagues**

lease | lēs | *n.* A written agreement that says how long a particular property is rented and how much money should be paid for it: *a three-year lease. v.* To rent: *will lease their house.* **leases, leased, leasing**

length | lĕngkth | *n.* The measure of how long a thing is: *a length of six feet.* **lengths, lengthen, lengthens, lengthened, lengthening, lengthy, lengthier, lengthiest**

lettuce | lĕt′ĭs | *n.* A green garden plant, often used in salads: *fresh lettuce from the garden.*

like | līk | *v.* To enjoy: *to like baseball.* **dislike, dislikes, disliked, disliking, dislikable**

limit | lĭm′ĭt | *v.* To restrict: *may limit his freedom. n.* **1.** An edge or farthest point: *the platform's limit.* **2.** The point beyond which one cannot go or do something: *a speed limit.* **limits, limited, limiting, limitless, limitation**

linen | lĭn′ən | *n.* A cloth or thread made from flax: *bought some linen.* **linens**

ă pat / ā pay / â care / ä father / ĕ pet / ē be / ĭ pit / ī pie / î fierce / ŏ pot / ō go / ô paw, for / oi oil / o͝o book / o͞o boot / ou out / ŭ cut / û fur / *th* the / th thin / hw which / zh vision / ə ago, item, pencil, atom, circus

©1977 by Houghton Mifflin Company. Reprinted by permission from THE AMERICAN HERITAGE SCHOOL DICTIONARY.

liquid | lĭk′wĭd | *n.* A fluid or substance that is neither a solid nor a gas: *a container of hot liquid.* ***liquids, liquefy, liquefies, liquefied, liquefying, liquidity, liquidness***

locate | lō′kāt′ | *v.* To find by searching or examining: *can't locate the leak.* ***locates, located, locating, location***

loss |lôs | *n.* A losing of something; a decrease: *a loss of energy.* ***losses***

loyal | loi′əl | *adj.* Faithful: *a loyal employee.* ***loyally, loyalty, loyalties, loyalism, loyalist***

M

machine | mə shēn′ | *n.* A device used for doing work, each part having a special function: *built a machine.* ***machines, machinery, machinist***

machinery | mə shē′nə rē | *n.* More than one machine: *fixed the machinery.* [see *machine*]

major | mā′jər | *adj.* Larger or greater: *a major amount. n.* An officer of the army, air force, or marines: *saluted the major.* ***majors, majored, majoring, majority, majorities***

manage | măn′ĭj | *v.* To succeed in accomplishing: *will manage to deliver it.* ***manages, managed, managing, manageable, manager, management***

manner | măn′ər | *n.* A way of doing something: *in an organized manner.* ***manners, mannered, mannerly, mannerism***

manual | măn′yōō əl | *n.* A handbook: *a helpful manual.* ***manuals, manually***

manufacture | măn′yə făk′chər | *v.* To make something by hand or by machine from raw materials: *to manufacture larger cars and trucks.* ***manufactures, manufactured, manufacturing, manufacturer***

manufacturing | măn′yə făk′chər ĭng | *adj.* Of or related to manufacturing: *a manufacturing center. n.* The process of making something from raw materials: *the manufacturing of glass.* [see *manufacture*]

margin | mär′jĭn | *n.* **1.** The blank space around a printed page: *will keep a straight margin.* **2.** Edge or border: *a margin of ribbon.* ***margins, margined, marginal, marginally***

mass | măs | *n.* **1.** A great quantity: *a mass of clouds.* **2.** A lump: *a mass of clay.* ***masses, massed, massing, massive***

material | mə tîr′ē əl | *n.* **1.** A fabric or cloth: *a soft material.* **2.** What a thing is made from: *material for building.* ***materials, materialize, materializes, materialized, materializing***

mean | mēn | *v.* To intend: *to mean nothing.* ***means, meant, meaning***

meant | mĕnt | *v.* Intended: *meant to go.* [see *mean*]

measure | mĕzh′ər | *n.* An amount or size: *a small measure of salt. v.* To find the amount or size of something: *will measure the window.* ***measures, measured, measuring, measurable, measurably, measurement***

medicine | mĕd′ĭ sĭn | *n.* A substance, usually a drug, used to treat or prevent disease: *the patient's medicine.* ***medicines, medical, medically, medicinal, medicate, medicates, medicated, medicating, medication, medic***

medium | mē′dē əm | *adj.* Middle in size, condition, or quality: *was set on medium speed.* ***mediums, media, median***

member | mĕm′bər | *n.* Anyone or anything belonging to a group: *a member of the team.* ***members, membership, memberships***

membership | mĕm′bər shĭp′ | *n.* The state of being a member: *continued her membership.* [see *member*]

memory | mĕm′ə rē | *n.* The ability to remember: *has an excellent memory.* ***memories, memorize, memorizes, memorized, memorizing, memorization***

metal | mĕt′l | *adj.* Made of metal: *a metal handle. n.* An element or substance that has a shine and can conduct electricity and heat easily: *a shiny metal.* ***metals, metallic***

meter | mē′tər | *n.* **1.** A device that measures and records the amount of electricity, gas, water, etc., used: *has read the meter.* **2.** A metric unit of length that equals 39.37 inches: *one meter in length.* ***meters, metered, metering, metric***

method | mĕth′əd | *n.* A way of doing something; procedure: *a slow method.* ***methods***

middle | mĭd′l | *n.* The halfway point; center: *the middle of the room.* ***midst, mid***

midst | mĭdst | *prep.* Among: *midst the cartons. n.* The middle: *in the midst of the field.* [see *middle*]

mine | mīn | v. To dig for gold, coal, etc.: *will mine for minerals.* **mines, mined, mining, miner, miners**

mineral | mĭn′ər əl | adj. Containing minerals: *mineral water.* n. A substance, such as coal, gold, or ores, obtained by mining: *a dull mineral.* **minerals, mineralize, mineralizes, mineralized, mineralizing, mineralogy, mineralogist**

mining | mī′nĭng | v. Digging for gold, coal, etc.: *was mining for gems.* adj. Of or for mining: *mining tools.* [see *mine*]

minor | mī′nər | adj. Lesser in importance; smaller: *caused a minor traffic delay.* **minors, minored, minoring, minority, minorities**

misery | mĭz′ə rē | n. Unhappiness or suffering: *a sigh of misery.* **miseries, miserable, miserably, miserableness**

motion | mō′shən | n. A movement: *a quick motion.* **motions, motioned, motioning, motionless**

muscle | mŭs′əl | n. 1. Body tissue with fibers that loosen or tighten to move parts of the body: *a strong muscle.* 2. Strength: *enough muscle for the job.* **muscles, muscled, muscling, muscular**

music | myoo′zĭk | The art of mixing sounds together in interesting arrangements: *played music.* **musical, musicals, musically, musician**

musical | myoo′zĭ kəl | adj. Accompanied by music: *a musical act.* n. A musical comedy: *saw the musical.* [see *music*]

mystery | mĭs′tə rē | adj. Of or related to a mystery: *mystery books.* n. 1. A novel or story about a strange event that is not explained until the end: *will read a mystery.* 2. Something that is unexplained or not understood: *the mystery of black holes.* **mysteries, mysterious, mysteriously**

N ███████████████████████

natural | năch′ər əl | adj. Made by nature: *a natural food.* [see *nature*]

nature | nā′chər | n. The world of living things and the outdoors: *enjoys nature.* **natures, natural, naturally, naturalist, naturalness**

necessary | nĕs′ĭ sĕr′ē | adj. Needed; essential: *necessary for good health.* **necessarily, necessitate, necessitates, necessitated, necessitating, necessity, necessities**

need | nēd | v. To want or lack: *will soon need water.* **needs, needed, needing, needy, needier, neediest, needless, needlessly, needlessness**

needless | nēd′lĭs | adj. Unnecessary: *needless worry.* [see *need*]

neglect | nĭ glĕkt′ | n. An act of giving little attention to: *ruined by neglect.* **neglects, neglected, neglecting, neglectful, neglectfully, negligent, negligence**

neighbor | nā′bər | n. A person who lives nearby: *visited the new neighbor.* **neighbors, neighboring, neighborly, neighborhood**

neighboring | nā′bər ĭng | adj. Nearby or bordering: *walked to the neighboring town.* [see *neighbor*]

neither | nē′thər | conj. A word used to show two negative choices: *neither you nor I.* pron. Not either one: *if neither spoke.*

nerve | nûrv | n. Courage: *lost her nerve.* **nerves, nerved, nerving, nervous, nervously, nervousness, nervy, nervier, nerviest**

nickel | nĭk′əl | n. A coin worth five cents in the U.S. and Canada: *found a nickel.* **nickels**

niece | nēs | n. A daughter of one's brother or sister: *my oldest niece.* **nieces**

noble | nō′bəl | adj. Great in character; generous: *a noble act.* n. A person of high rank or title: *a noble of the court.* **nobler, noblest, nobly, nobles, nobility, nobleness**

normal | nôr′məl | adj. Usual or typical: *a normal day.* **normally, normalize, normalcy, normality**

ă **pat** / ā **pay** / â **care** / ä **father** / ĕ **pet** / ē **be** / ĭ **pit** / ī **pie** / î **fierce** / ŏ **pot** / ō **go** / ô **paw, for** / oi **oil** / oo **book** /
oo **boot** / ou **out** / ŭ **cut** / û **fur** / *th* **the** / th **thin** / hw **which** / zh **vision** / ə **ago, item, pencil, atom, circus**
©1977 by Houghton Mifflin Company. Reprinted by permission from THE AMERICAN HERITAGE SCHOOL DICTIONARY.

notice | **nō′**tĭs | *n.* **1.** Attention: *showed little notice.* **2.** An important warning or message: *will read the notice.* *v.* To see or give attention to: *didn't notice your new sweater.* **notices, noticed, noticing, noticeable, noticeably, notable, notably**

nowhere | **nō′**hwâr′ | *n.* Not anywhere: *nowhere to go.*

O

obey | ō **bā′** | *v.* To do what one is told: *will obey the command.* **obeys, obeyed, obeying, obedient, obediently, obedience**

object | əb **jĕkt′** | *v.* To oppose: *to object to the decision.* — | **ob′**jĭkt | *n.* Anything that can be seen or touched: *the wooden object.* **objects, objected, objecting, objection, objectionable, objectionably**

observation | ŏb′zûr **vā′**shən | *adj.* Of or related to observation: *an observation post on the mountain.* *n.* Something seen: *a close observation.* [see *observe*]

observe | əb **zûrv′** | *v.* To watch or see: *will observe the animals.* **observes, observed, observing, observation, observations, observational, observer, observatory, observant, observable**

obtain | əb **tān′** | *v.* To get by effort: *can obtain skills.* **obtains, obtained, obtaining, obtainable, obtainer, obtainment**

onion | **ŭn′**yən | *adj.* Of an onion: *an onion flavor.* *n.* A strong-smelling vegetable with a bulb: *a slice of onion.* **onions**

opera | **ŏp′**ər ə | *n.* A play in which music, played by an orchestra, is a major part: *enjoyed the opera.* **operas, operatic, operetta**

operate | **ŏp′**ə rāt′ | *v.* **1.** To work or function effectively: *won't operate in the heat.* **2.** To perform surgery: *will operate on the patient today.* **operates, operated, operating, operation, operations, operational, operator**

operation | ŏp′ə **rā′**shən | *n.* **1.** An action or activity: *a simple operation.* **2.** Surgery: *in the hospital for an operation.* [see *operate*]

oppose | ə **pōz′** | *v.* To be against: *to oppose the ruling.* **opposes, opposed, opposing, opposite, opposites, oppositely, opposition, oppositeness**

opposite | **ŏp′**ə zĭt | *adj.* As different as possible: *opposite opinions.* [see *oppose*]

organize | **ôr′**gə nīz | *v.* **1.** To combine into a group: *will organize a tour group.* **2.** To arrange in an orderly way: *to organize the papers.* **organizes, organized, organizing, organizer, organization**

otherwise | **ŭth′**ər wīz′ | *adv.* **1.** Under other circumstances: *would have lost otherwise.* **2.** Differently: *shown otherwise.* *conj.* Or else: *otherwise I'll do it.*

overflow | **ō′**vər flō′ | *v.* To spill over: *if the sink will overflow.* **overflows, overflowed, overflowing**

P

pack | păk | *v.* To put into a bag or container for storing, selling, etc.: *to pack the dishes.* **unpack, unpacks, unpacked, unpacking, unpacker**

paragraph | **păr′**ə grăf′ | *n.* A group of sentences relating to the same idea and forming a division on a page: *wrote a new paragraph.* **paragraphs, paragraphed, paragraphing**

passage | **păs′**ĭj | *n.* **1.** A part of a speech, writing, or musical composition: *selected a passage* **2.** The act of passing: *the passage of cars.* **passages, passaged, passaging, passenger**

patent | **păt′**nt | *v.* To obtain a legal document claiming sole rights to an invention: *will patent the new machine.* *n.* A government document that gives someone the sole rights to make or sell an invention for a certain number of years: *the inventor's patent.* **patents, patented, patenting**

pattern | **păt′**ərn | *n.* A model or guide used to help make something: *used the pattern.* **patterns, patterned, patterning**

pause | pôz | *v.* To wait or stop for a short time: *didn't pause at the door.* **pauses, paused, pausing**

pave | pāv | *v.* To cover with pavement: *will pave the driveway.* **paves, paved, paving, pavement, pavements**

pavement | **pāv′**mənt | *n.* A surface for streets, sidewalks, etc., that consists of concrete, asphalt, or stones: *on the pavement.* [see *pave*]

peer | pîr | *v.* To look closely at; gaze: *to peer at the photograph.* **peers, peered, peering**

percent | pər **sĕnt′** | *n.* The parts in each hundred; hundredths: *eighty percent correct.* **percents, percentage, percentages**

perform | pər **fôrm′** | *v.* To act or do tricks in public: *will perform before an audience.* **performs, performed, performing, performer, performance**

permanent | **pûr′**mə nənt | *adj.* Lasting: *a permanent change.* **permanently, permanence, permanency**

permission | pər **mĭsh′**ən | *n.* Consent: *gave her permission.* [see *permit*]

permit | pûr **mĭt′** | *v.* To allow: *will permit them to go.* **permits, permitted, permitting, permissive, permissively, permissible, permissiveness, permission**

permitted | pər **mĭt′**tĭd | *v.* Allowed: *permitted to enter.* [see *permit*]

person | **pûr′**sən | *n.* A human being: *a tall person.* **persons, personal, personally, personable, personalize, personality**

personal | **pûr′**sə nəl | *adj.* Private or of a person: *his personal library.* [see *person*]

photograph | **fō′**tə grăf′ | *n.* A picture taken by a camera: *a recent photograph.* **photographs, photographed, photographing, photo, photography, photographer**

pickle | **pĭk′**əl | *n.* A cucumber that has been preserved in salt water or vinegar: *a sour pickle.* **pickles, pickled, pickling**

pier | pîr | *n.* A walkway that extends into the water and is supported by columns: *fished from the pier.* **piers**

pity | **pĭt′**ē | *n.* Distress or sorrow for another: *felt pity for the sick child.* **pities, pitied, pitying, pityingly, pitiful, pitifully, piteous, piteously**

plan | plăn | *v.* To design or think out ahead of time: *will plan a vacation.* **plans, planned, planning, planner**

plank | plăngk | *n.* A long piece of sawed wood: *will split a plank.* **planks**

planned | plănd | *v.* Designed or thought out ahead of time: *planned a trip.* [see *plan*]

pleasant | **plĕz′**ənt | *adj.* **1.** Agreeable: *a pleasant houseguest.* **2.** Delightful; giving pleasure: *a pleasant sound.* **pleasantly, pleasantry, pleasantness**

pleasure | **plĕzh′**ər | *n.* Enjoyment or delight: *the pleasure of reading.* **pleasures, pleasured, pleasuring, pleasurable, pleasurably, pleasureful**

pledge | plĕj | *v.* To promise: *will pledge their loyalty. n.* A formal promise: *honored the pledge.* **pledges, pledged, pledging**

plunge | plŭnj | *v.* To throw oneself suddenly into water, a place, etc.: *to plunge into darkness. n.* The act of plunging: *a graceful plunge.* **plunges, plunged, plunging, plunger, plungers**

polish | **pŏl′**ĭsh | *n.* A substance used to make something shine: *an oily polish. v.* To make something shine: *will polish the table.* **polishes, polished, polishing, polisher**

polite | pə **līt** | *adj.* Showing good manners: *a polite request.* **politely, politeness**

porter | **pôr′**tər | *n.* A person who is employed to carry luggage: *called the porter.* **porters**

positive | **pŏz′**ĭ tĭv | *adj.* **1.** Showing agreement; approving: *a positive attitude.* **2.** Absolutely certain: *positive of her skill.* **positively, postiveness**

possible | **pŏs′**ə bəl | *adj.* Capable of happening: *a possible win.* **impossible, impossibly, impossibility, impossibilities, impossibleness**

post | pōst | *n.* The mail: *delivered by post.* **posts, posted, posting, postal, postage**

postage | **pō′**stĭj | *n.* The amount charged on anything sent by mail: *thirty cents for postage.* **–Postage stamp–**A stamp for sending something by mail. [see *post*]

postpone | pōst **pōn′** | *v.* To delay; put off: *will postpone until tomorrow.* **postpones, postponed, postponing, postponement**

poultry | **pōl′**trē | *adj.* Of or related to poultry: *a poultry dinner. n.* Birds such as chickens, turkeys, etc., used as food: *cooking poultry.*

ă pat / ā pay / â care / ä father / ĕ pet / ē be / ĭ pit / ī pie / î fierce / ŏ pot / ō go / ô paw, for / oi oil / ōō book /
ōō boot / ou out / ŭ cut / û fur / *th* the / th thin / hw which / zh vision / ə ago, item, pencil, atom, circus
©1977 by Houghton Mifflin Company. Reprinted by permission from THE AMERICAN HERITAGE SCHOOL DICTIONARY.

power | **pou′ər** | *n.* Force or strength: *the machine's power.* **powers, powered, powering, powerful, powerfully, powerfulness, powerless, powerlessly, powerlessness**

powerful | **pou′ər fəl** | *adj.* Strong or forceful: *a powerful athlete.* [see *power*]

practical | **prăk′tĭ kəl** | *adj.* Useful: *practical advice.* [see *practice*]

practice | **prăk′tĭs** | *v.* To do something over and over again for improvement: *to practice his singing. n.* The action repeated many times to improve a skill: *long hours of practice.* **practices, practiced, practicing, practical, practically, practicality, practicalness**

prepare | **prĭ pär′** | *v.* To make ready for a certain purpose, event, etc.: *will prepare the speech.* **prepares, prepared, preparing, preparatory, preparedly, preparedness, preparation, preparations**

present | **prĭ zĕnt′** | *v.* **1.** To give: *to present the grand prize.* **2.** To offer for thought or consideration: *to present the problem.* **presents, presented, presenting, presentable, presentably, presently, presentation**

presented | **prĭ zĕn′tĭd** | *v.* **1.** Gave: *presented the check.* **2.** Offered for thought or consideration: *presented for discussion.* [see *present*]

prevent | **prĭ vĕnt′** | *v.* To keep from occurring: *might prevent a fire.* **prevents, prevented, preventing, preventable, preventative, preventive, preventiveness, prevention**

primary | **prī′mĕr′ē** | *adj.* First in order or importance: *a primary issue.* **—Primary color**—A color belonging to a group that produces all other colors when mixed together. [see *prime*]

prime | **prīm** | *adj.* The first in importance: *a prime reason.* **primes, primed, priming, primer, primarily, primely, primary, primaries**

prison | **prĭz′ən** | *n.* **1.** A building where criminals are housed: *sentenced to a prison.* **2.** A place where one is kept against one's will: *if the room became a prison.* **prisons, prisoner, prisoners**

prisoner | **prĭz′ə nər** | *n.* **1.** A person held unwillingly: *kept as a prisoner.* **2.** A person under arrest or in jail: *guarded the prisoner.* **—Prisoner of war**—A person taken by the enemy in wartime. [see *prison*]

private | **prī′vĭt** | *adj.* Not for public use: *a private path.* **privates, privately, privacy**

proceed | **prə sēd′** | *v.* **1.** To move forward after having stopped: *will proceed on the trail.* **2.** to continue; carry on some action: *will proceed to speak.* **proceeds, proceeded, proceeding, procedural, procedure**

produce | **prə dōōs′** | *v.* **1.** To make: *to produce cars.* **2.** To bring forth: *will produce fruit.* **produces, produced, producing, producible, productive, productively, product, production, productivity, producer**

profit | **prŏf′ĭt** | *v.* To benefit or gain: *will profit from the sale. n.* The financial gain made from a business: *a day's profit.* **profits, profited, profiting, profitable, profitably**

project | **prŏj′ĕkt′** | *n.* A special assignment carried out by students: *a history project.* **projects, projected, projecting, projector**

proof | **prōōf** | *n.* A way of showing beyond a doubt the truth of something: *pictures as proof.* [see *prove*]

proper | **prŏp′ər** | *adj.* Correct: *proper speech.* **properly**

properly | **prŏp′ər lē** | *adv.* Correctly: *properly done.* [see *proper*]

prove | **prōōv** | *v.* To show the truth of something: *hard to prove his story.* **proves, proved, proving, proven, proof**

provide | **prə vīd′** | *v.* To supply what is needed: *will provide a home.* **provides, provided, providing, provision, provisions, provider**

provisions | **prə vĭzh′ənz** | *n.* Food supplies: *provisions for the voyage.* [see *provide*]

publish | **pŭb′lĭsh** | *v.* To print matter for sale or distribution: *will publish the novel.* **publishes, published, publishing, publisher, publication**

punctual | **pŭngk′ chōō əl** | *adj.* On time: *a punctual arrival.* **punctually, punctualness**

punish | **pŭn′ĭsh** | *v.* To cause pain or discomfort for some wrongdoing: *to punish the known thief.* **punishes, punished, punishing, punishable, punisher, punishment**

purchase | **pûr′chĭs** | *v.* To buy: *will purchase a house. n.* A buying of something: *a wise purchase.* **purchases, purchased, purchasing, purchaser**

purple | **pûr′pəl** | *adj.* Of the color purple: *a purple dress. n.* A color made up of a mix of blue and red: *chose purple.* **purples, purpled, purpling, purplish**

purpose | **pûr′pəs** | *n.* The reason for something: *the purpose of the speech.* **purposes, purposely, purposeful, purposefully, purposefulness, purposeless**

Q

quiet | **kwī′ĭt** | *adj.* Making little noise: *a quiet library room.* **quiets, quieted, quieting, quieter, quietest, quietly, quietness**

quietly | **kwī′ĭt lē** | *adv.* Without much noise: *moved quietly.* [see *quiet*]

R

radiate | **rā′dē āt′** | *v.* To give out rays: *will radiate heat.* **radiates, radiated, radiating, radiant, radiantly, radiance, radiation, radiator**

radiation | **rā′dē ā′shən** | *n.* The process of giving out rays of heat, light, or other energy: *nuclear radiation.* [see *radiate*]

raid | **rād** | *n.* A surprise attack: *a midnight raid.* **raids, raided, raiding, raider**

raisin | **rā′zən** | *n.* A dried grape: *a sweet raisin.* **raisins**

rapid | **răp′ĭd** | *adj.* Very fast: *a rapid motion.* **rapids, rapidly, rapidness, rapidity**

rapidly | **răp′ĭd lē** | *adv.* Very quickly: *spoke rapidly.* [see *rapid*]

rascal | **răs′kəl** | *n.* A mischievous person; scamp: *a young rascal.* **rascals, rascally**

rate | **rāt** | *v.* To judge or grade: *will rate the quality. n.* A class or grade: *third rate.* **rates, rated, rating, ratings, ratio, ration**

rating | **rā′tĭng** | *v.* Judging or grading: *rating the papers. n.* A position in a class or grade: *a low rating.* [see *rate*]

realize | **rē′ə līz′** | *v.* To understand fully: *doesn't realize the danger.* **realizes, realized, realizing, realization**

realizes | **rē′ə lī′ zĭz** | *v.* Fully understands: *realizes the problem.* [see *realize*]

receive | **rĭ sēv′** | *v.* To get: *receive a gift.* **receives, received, receiving, receiver, receipt**

received | **rĭ sēvd′** | *v.* Got: *received a party invitation.* [see *receive*]

recent | **rē′sənt** | *adj.* Not long ago: *a recent experience.* **recently, recentness, recency**

reckless | **rĕk′lĭs** | *adj.* Careless: *a reckless driver.* **recklessly, recklessness**

reduce | **rĭ dōōs′** | *v.* To make less or smaller: *to reduce the amount.* **reduces, reduced, reducing, reducible, reducer, reduction**

reflect | **rĭ flĕkt′** | *v.* To form an image from a light that turns back after striking a surface: *will reflect her happy face.* **reflects, reflected, reflecting, reflection, reflections, reflector**

reflection | **rĭ flĕk′ shən** | *n.* A likeness or image formed by light turned back from a surface: *his reflection in the glass.* [see *reflect*]

reform | **rĭ fôrm′** | *v.* To improve: *to reform the law. n.* A movement or policy to make something better: *a government reform.* **reforms, reformed, reforming, reformer, reformatory, reformation**

refuse | **rĭ fyōōz′** | *v.* To decline; reject: *won't refuse the help.* — | **rĕf′yōōs** | *n.* Waste material; garbage: *to throw out the refuse.* **refuses, refused, refusing, refusal**

regard | **rĭ gärd′** | *n.* Consideration or careful thought: *regard toward others.* **regards, regarded, regarding, regardless, regardlessly**

relate | **rĭ lāt′** | *v.* To have a connection to: *can't relate the issues.* **relates, related, relating, relative, relatives, relatively, relation**

relative | **rĕl′ə tĭv** | *n.* A person belonging to the same family as another: *a relative of mine.* [see *relate*]

ă pat / ā pay / â care / ä father / ĕ pet / ē be / ĭ pit / ī pie / î fierce / ŏ pot / ō go / ô paw, for / oi oil / ōō book /
ōō boot / ou out / ŭ cut / û fur / *th* the / th thin / hw which / zh vision / ə ago, item, pencil, atom, circus
©1977 by Houghton Mifflin Company. Reprinted by permission from THE AMERICAN HERITAGE SCHOOL DICTIONARY.

release | rǐ **lēs′** | v. To let go of: *to release its hold.* n. A setting free: *the release of the zoo animals.* **releases, released, releasing**

reliable | rǐ **lī′ə bəl** | adj. Dependable: *a reliable student.* [see *rely*]

rely | rǐ **lī′** | v. To depend on: *can rely on me.* **relies, relied, relying, reliable, reliably, reliability**

represent | rĕp′rǐ **zěnt′** | v. To speak for: *will represent him in the court trial tomorrow.* **represents, represented, representing, representative, representation**

republic | rǐ **pŭb′lǐk** | n. A government in which citizens elect representatives: *formed a new republic.* **republics, republican**

resolve | rǐ **sŏlv′** | v. To answer and explain: *will resolve the question.* **resolves, resolved, resolving, resolvable, resolution, resolver**

resort | rǐ **zôrt′** | n. A place where people go for recreation: *a beautiful resort.* **resorts, resorted, resorting**

respect | rǐ **spěkt′** | n. Honor: *respect for the hero.* **respects, respected, respecting, respectful, respectfully, respectable, respectably, respectability**

response | rǐ **spŏns′** | n. An answer: *an excellent response from the student.* **responses, responsible, responsibility**

result | rǐ **zŭlt′** | n. A consequence or outcome: *the test result.* **results, resulted, resulting**

retreat | rǐ **trēt′** | v. To withdraw from: *to retreat from the fire.* n. A withdrawing from an enemy attack: *a sudden retreat.* **retreats, retreated, retreating**

reverse | rǐ **vûrs′** | v. **1.** To change to the opposite: *will reverse our position on the issue.* **2.** To turn the opposite way: *to reverse the car.* **reverses, reversed, reversing, reversible, reversibility, reversely, reversal**

rinse | rǐns | v. To wash only lightly: *will rinse the cups.* **rinses, rinsed, rinsing**

rot | rŏt | v. To spoil or decay: *will rot in the heat.* **rots, rotted, rotting, rotten, rottener, rottenest, rottenly, rottenness**

rotten | rŏt′n | adj. Spoiled or decayed: *a rotten banana.* [see *rot*]

rudder | rŭd′ər | n. A plate of wood or metal attached to the back of a boat to help steer it: *the sailboat's rudder.* **rudders**

rude | rood | adj. **1.** Roughly made: *a rude model.* **2.** Impolite: *a rude customer.* **ruder, rudest, rudely, rudeness**

runaway | **rŭn′ə wā′** | adj. Out of control: *a runaway carriage.* n. A person or thing that runs away: *chased the runaway.* **runaways**

S

salad | **săl′əd** | n. A mixture of vegetables: *a delicious salad.* **salads**

salesperson | **sālz′ pûr′sən** | n. A person who sells for a living: *a helpful salesperson.* **salespeople**

salute | sə **loot′** | v. To show respect by a certain gesture: *to salute the officer.* **salutes, saluted, saluting, saluter, salutation**

sandwich | **sănd′wǐch** | n. Two or more slices of bread with meat or filling between them: *a delicious sandwich.* **sandwiches, sandwiched, sandwiching**

satisfied | **săt′ǐs fīd′** | adj. Pleased: *a satisfied worker.* v. Put an end to: *satisfied their thirst.* [see *satisfy*]

satisfy | **săt′ǐs fī′** | v. **1.** To please: *to satisfy his parents.* **2.** To put an end to: *to satisfy my curiosity.* **satisfies, satisfied, satisfying, satisfyingly, satisfactory, satisfactorily, satisfaction**

scarce | skârs | adj. Not enough to meet a demand: *a scarce amount of water.* **scarcer, scarcest, scarcely, scarceness, scarcity**

scarcely | **skârs′lē** | adv. Barely: *scarcely able to finish.* [see *scarce*]

scatter | **skăt′ər** | v. To sprinkle; throw here and there: *will scatter the crumbs.* **scatters, scattered, scattering**

scene | sēn | n. **1.** The place where something happened: *scene of the accident.* **2.** A view: *the scene from the window.* **scenes, scenic, scenery**

scissors | **sǐz′ərz** | n. An instrument with two blades for cutting: *trimmed with the scissors.*

scramble | **skrăm′bəl** | v. To crawl or climb: *to scramble over the rocks.* **scrambles, scrambled, scrambling, scrambler**

scratch | skrăch | v. **1.** To rub to relieve itching: *to scratch his insect bite.* **2.** To mark or cut with something sharp: *won't scratch the wood.* **scratches, scratched, scratching, scratchy, scratchier, scratchiest, scratchiness, scratcher**

screwdriver | skroo′drī′vər | n. A tool that tightens or loosens screws by turning: *used a screwdriver to fix the shelf.* **screwdrivers**

search | sûrch | v. To look over carefully in order to find something lost or hidden: *to search in the house.* n. The act of looking for something: *a careful search.* **searches, searched, searching, searchingly, searcher**

seldom | sĕl′dəm | adv. Rarely: *seldom happy.* **seldomly**

select | sĭ lĕkt′ | v. To choose: *will select a partner.* **selects, selected, selecting, selective, selectively, selectness, selection, selections**

selection | sĭ lĕk′shən | n. **1.** A group of people or things chosen to be representative, or a sample: *a selection of shoes.* **2.** A choice: *an excellent selection of magazines.* [see *select*]

selfish | sĕl′fĭsh | adj. Showing concern only for oneself: *a selfish act.* **selfishly, selfishness**

senior | sēn′yər | n. A student in the graduating class of a high school or college: *gave congratulations to the senior.* adj. Older: *a senior member.* **seniors, seniority**

separate | sĕp′ər ĭt′ | adj. Divided: *separate rooms.* —| sĕp′ə rāt′ | v. To divide or keep apart: *to separate the group.* **separates, separated, separating, separately, separable, separator, separateness, separation**

serious | sîr′ē əs | adj. Thoughtful or grave: *a serious mood.* **seriously, seriousness**

servant | sûr′vənt | n. A person hired to work in someone else's household: *employed a servant.* [see *serve*]

serve | sûrv | n. The putting of a ball in play by hitting it: *a strong serve.* v. **1.** To work for: *to serve the family loyally.* **2.** To present food to others: *to serve lunch.* **serves, served, serving, server, servant, servants, service**

settle | sĕt′l | v. To establish a colony: *to settle in America.* **settles, settled, settling, settler, settlement, settlements**

settlement | sĕt′l mənt | n. A colony: *a British settlement.* [see *settle*]

several | sĕv′ər əl | adj. Some or few: *several questions.*

severe | sə vîr′ | adj. Harsh: *severe conditions.* **severer, severest, severely, severity, severeness**

sheriff | shĕr′ĭf | n. The chief law-enforcing officer of a county: *elected a sheriff.* **sheriffs**

shoulder | shōl′dər | n. The part of the body between the neck and upper arm: *scratched his shoulder.* **shoulders, shouldered, shouldering**

sick | sĭk | adj. Ill; not healthy: *was feeling sick.* **sicker, sickest, sickly, sicken, sickens, sickened, sickening, sickeningly**

sicken | sĭk′ən | v. To make or become ill: *might sicken the viewer.* [see *sick*]

silent | sī′lənt | adj. Without speech: *a silent classroom.* **silently, silence, silences, silenced, silencing, silencer**

simple | sĭm′pəl | adj. Plain; easy: *a simple task.* **simpler, simplest, simplify, simplifies, simplified, simplifying, simplicity, simply**

simply | sĭm′plē | adv. Plainly; easily: *simply written.* [see *simple*]

skeleton | skĕl′ĭ tən | adj. Relating to a skeleton: *skeleton structure.* n. The supporting structure of bones in the body that protects tissues, muscles, etc.: *examined the skeleton.* **skeletons, skeletal**

slight | slīt | adj. Not much; little: *a slight fever.* **slights, slighted, slighting, slighter, slightest, slightly, slightness**

slip | slĭp | v. To put on or take off easily: *will slip on a blouse.* **slips, slipped, slipping, slipper, slippers, slippery, slipperiness**

slippers | slĭp′ərz | n. Light shoes that can be slipped on and off easily: *a robe and slippers.* [see *slip*]

ă pat / ā pay / â care / ä father / ĕ pet / ē be / ĭ pit / ī pie / î fierce / ŏ pot / ō go / ô paw, for / oi oil / oo book / oo boot / ou out / ŭ cut / û fur / th the / th thin / hw which / zh vision / ə ago, item, pencil, atom, circus

slither | slĭ*th*′ər | *v.* To move with a sliding motion: *to slither along the floor.* **slithers, slithered, slithering, slithery**

sole | sōl | *n.* The bottom part of a shoe, boot, etc.: *replaced the sole.* **soles, soled, soling**

solo | sō′lō | *adj.* Alone; without a partner: *a solo performance.* **solos, soloist**

solve | sŏlv | *v.* To explain: *will solve the problem.* **solves, solved, solving, solvable, solver**

solving | sŏl′vĭng | *v.* Explaining: *solving the riddle.* [see *solve*]

source | sôrs | *n.* **1.** The place or person from which something comes: *a source of information.* **2.** The beginning of a river, stream, etc.: *swam to the source.* **sources**

spade | spād | *v.* To dig with a spade: *will spade the field. n.* A digging tool that has a long handle and an iron blade which can be pushed down into the ground with one's foot: *a shovel and spade.* **spades, spaded, spading**

spare | spâr | *adj.* Extra: *spare keys.* **spares, spared, sparing, sparingly, spareness**

speak | spēk | *v.* To talk: *to speak clearly.* **speaks, spoke, speaking, spoken, speaker, speakers**

speaker | spē′kər | *n.* A person who is talking: *a timid speaker.* [see *speak*]

special | spĕsh′əl | *adj.* Unusual: *a special yearly event.* **specials, specialize, specializes, specialized, specializing, specialization, specialty, specialist**

speech | spēch | *n.* A talk, especially one prepared for an audience: *an entertaining speech.* **speeches, speechless**

spirit | spĭr′ĭt | *n.* Enthusiasm: *full of spirit.* **spirits, spirited, spiritual, spiritless**

spite | spīt | *n.* Ill will: *due to spite.* **—In spite of—**Despite. **spites, spited, spiting, spiteful, spitefully, spitefulness**

splendid | splĕn′dĭd | *adj.* Grand; wonderful: *a splendid view.* **splendidly, splendidness**

spoil | spoil | *v.* To become rotten or unusable: *if the vegetables spoil.* **spoils, spoiled, spoiling, spoiler**

sprang | sprăng | *v.* Leaped or jumped: *sprang over the fence.* [see *spring*]

spread | sprĕd | *v.* To cover with a thin layer: *will spread the jam. n.* Any soft food that can be spread: *a tasty spread.* **spreads, spreading, spreader**

spring | sprĭng | *v.* To leap or jump: *to spring up.* **springs, sprang, sprung, springing, springy, springier, springiest**

sprinkle | sprĭng′kəl | *n.* A light rain: *an afternoon sprinkle.* **sprinkles, sprinkled, sprinkling, sprinkler**

squash | skwŏsh | *n.* A fruit related to the pumpkin and cucumber: *cooked the yellow squash.* **squashes, squashed, squashing, squashy, squashier, squashiest, squashiness**

squeeze | skwēz | *v.* **1.** To force one's way through something: *to squeeze through the tiny opening.* **2.** To grip: *to squeeze your hand.* **squeezes, squeezed, squeezing, squeezable, squeezer**

staff | stăf | *n.* A group of employees: *a memo to the staff.* **staffs, staffed, staffing**

standard | stăn′dərd | *adj.* Normal or accepted size, amount, quality, etc.: *a standard cost. n.* A model or basis of comparison: *a standard of excellence.* **standards**

stare | stâr | *v.* To look long and directly at someone or something: *will stare at the mirror.* **stares, stared, staring**

starve | stärv | *v.* To die due to hunger: *if the dog should starve.* **starves, starved, starving, starvation**

stationary | stā′shə nĕr′ē | *adj.* Not moving: *stationary traffic.*

statue | stăch′ōō | *n.* An image of someone or something that is formed out of wood, stone, clay, etc.: *a famous statue.* **statues, statuette**

steady | stĕd′ē | *adj.* **1.** Firm; not shaking: *a steady balance.* **2.** Regular: *a steady client.* **steadies, steadied, steadying, steadier, steadiest, steadily, steadiness**

steer | stîr | *v.* To direct or guide the course of something: *can't steer the bicycle.* **steers, steered, steering, steerer, steerable**

sting | stĭng | *v.* To wound with a sharp organ, such as that of certain insects: *will sting her foot.* **stings, stung, stinging, stinger**

stingy | stĭn′jē | *adj.* Ungenerous: *a stingy contribution.* **stingier, stingiest, stingily, stinginess**

stitch | stĭch | v. To sew: *to stitch the shirt. n.* A link, knot, or loop made by sewing or knitting: *a tiny stitch.* **stitches, stitched, stitching, stitcher**

stomach | stŭm'ək | adj. Related to or of the stomach: *stomach pains. n.* The organ in the body which digests food: *a full stomach.* **stomachs**

strange | strānj | adj. Unknown: *a strange neighborhood.* **stranger, strangest, strangely, strangeness, strangers**

stranger | strān'jər | n. An unknown person: *a stranger at the party.* [see *strange*]

strength | strĕngkth | n. Power or force: *the strength of twenty-five people.* **strengths, strengthen, strengthens, strengthened, strengthening, strengthener**

stretch | strĕch | v. **1.** To extend to full length: *wants to stretch her arms.* **2.** To cause to last: *will stretch the few supplies.* **stretches, stretched, stretching, stretchy, stretchier, stretchiest, stretchable, stretchiness, stretcher**

strict | strĭkt | adj. Stern; harsh: *strict rules.* **stricter, strictest, strictly, strictness**

stroll | strōl | v. To walk for pleasure: *may stroll in the park. n.* A quiet, pleasurable walk: *a stroll after dinner.* **strolls, strolled, strolling, stroller**

struggle | strŭg'əl | n. A great effort: *a struggle to stand.* **struggles, struggled, struggling, struggler**

stupid | stōō'pĭd | adj. Not intelligent: *a stupid look.* **stupider, stupidest, stupidly, stupidity**

style | stīl | n. Fashion: *a particular style.* **styles, styled, styling, stylish, stylishly, stylishness, stylist, styler**

stylish | stī'lĭsh | adj. Fashionable: *a stylish dress.* [see *style*]

subject | sŭb'jĭkt | n. **1.** In grammar, a word or words about which something is said: *subject and verb.* **2.** A topic: *historical subject.* — | səb jĕkt' | v. To cause to experience: *may subject to testing.* **subjects, subjected, subjecting**

submarine | sŭb'mə rēn' | n. A ship that can go underwater: *a nuclear submarine.* **submarines**

submit | səb mĭt' | v. **1.** To make available; offer: *to submit the paper to the teacher.* **2.** To give up; surrender: *will submit to the winners.* **submits, submitted, submitting**

succeed | sək sēd' | v. To do well: *to succeed in high school.* **succeeds, succeeded, succeeding, success, successful, successfully, successfulness**

sudden | sŭd'n | adj. Unexpected: *a sudden noise.* **suddenly, suddenness**

suddenly | sŭd'n lē | adv. Unexpectedly: *left suddenly.* [see *sudden*]

suffer | sŭf'ər | v. To have pain or grief: *to suffer from a fever.* **suffers, suffered, suffering, sufferer**

suggest | səg jĕst' | v. To propose or offer as an idea: *may suggest a movie.* **suggests, suggested, suggesting, suggestive, suggestion, suggestions**

suit | sōōt | v. To be appropriate for: *to suit their needs.* **suits, suited, suiting, suitable, suitably, suitableness, suitability**

suitable | sōō'tə bəl | adj. Proper; appropriate: *a suitable jacket.* [see *suit*]

supply | sə plī' | n. A ready-for-use quantity of something: *a large supply of meat. v.* To provide what is missing or lacking: *will supply paper and pens.* **supplies, supplied, supplying, supplier**

support | sə pôrt' | v. To hold up: *will support the roof.* **supports, supported, supporting, supportive, supportable, supporter**

supreme | sə prēm' | adj. The greatest in degree or quality: *supreme happiness.* **supremely, supremeness, supremacy**

surface | sûr'fəs | n. The outermost layer of something: *the earth's surface. v.* To rise to the top: *if the fish will surface for food.* **surfaces, surfaced, surfacing**

ă pat / ā pay / â care / ä father / ĕ pet / ē be / ĭ pit / ī pie / î fierce / ŏ pot / ō go / ô paw, for / oi oil / ōō book / ōō boot / ou out / ŭ cut / û fur / th the / th thin / hw which / zh vision / ə ago, item, pencil, atom, circus

suspect | sə spĕkt′ | v. **1.** To imagine to be so: *to suspect a trick.* **2.** To believe guilty: *won't suspect those people.* —| sŭs′pĕkt′ | n. A person thought to have committed a crime: *followed the likely suspect.* **suspects, suspected, suspecting, suspicious, suspiciously, suspicion, suspiciousness**

swift | swĭft | adj. Quick or rapid: *a swift current.* **swifter, swiftest, swiftly, swiftness**

swiftly | swĭft′lē | adv. Quickly: *walked swiftly.* [see *swift*]

switch | swĭch | n. A device used to open or close an electrical circuit: *pressed the switch.* v. To exchange: *will switch seats.* **switches, switched, switching, switcher**

system | sĭs′təm | n. **1.** A set of parts or elements that work together to form a whole: *an electrical system.* **2.** A plan or method of operation: *my system for studying for a test.* **systems, systematic, systematize**

T

tailor | tā′lər | n. A person who sews or mends clothes: *a skillful tailor.* **tailors, tailored, tailoring**

taxi | tăk′sē | n. A car for hire with a meter to charge mileage: *will call a taxi.* **taxis, taxied, taxiing**

taxis | tăk′ sēz | n. More than one taxi: *a line of taxis.* [see *taxi*]

telegraph | tĕl′ə grăf′ | adj. Of a telegraph: *the telegraph code book.* n. A system of communication in which a message is sent by either wire or radio: *received by telegraph.* **telegraphs, telegraphed, telegraphing, telegraphic, telegrapher, telegraphy**

telephone | tĕl′ə fōn′ | n. An instrument for sending sound or speech at a distance: *dialed the telephone.* **telephones, telephoned, telephoning**

television | tĕl′ə vĭzh′ən | adj. Of television: *a television station.* n. A device that receives radio waves or electrical signals and reproduces them on a screen: *a portable color television.* **televisions, televise, televises, televised, televising**

term | tûrm | n. A period of time in which something lasts: *spring term at school.* **terms, termed, terming**

terrible | tĕr′ə bəl | adj. **1.** Extremely bad: *a terrible headache.* **2.** Dreadful or awful: *a terrible noise.* **terribly, terribleness**

territory | tĕr′ĭ tôr′ē | n. **1.** An animal's nesting area: *the lion's territory.* **2.** Region or land: *ruled the territory.* **territories, territorial, territorialize**

terror | tĕr′ər | n. Extreme fear: *felt terror in the crowd.* **terrors, terrorize, terrorizes, terrorized, terrorizing, terrorizer, terrorist, terrorism**

theater | thē′ə tər | n. A place where plays are performed or movies are shown: *go to the theater.* **theaters, theatrical, theatrics**

thief | thēf | n. A person who steals: *arrested the thief.* **thieve, thieves, thieved, thieving, thievish, thievery, theft**

think | thĭngk | v. To use the mind: *will think about the problem.* **thinks, thought, thinking, thoughtful, thoughtfully, thoughtfulness, thoughts, thoughtless, thoughtlessly, thoughtlessness**

thirst | thûrst | n. A dry feeling in the mouth and throat, caused by the lack of anything to drink: *will satisfy their thirst.* **thirsts, thirsted, thirsting, thirsty, thirstier, thirstiest, thirstily, thirstiness**

thirsty | thûr′ stē | adj. Feeling thirst, or a need for a drink: *a thirsty runner.* [see *thirst*]

thoughtful | thôt′fəl | adj. **1.** Thinking; full of thought: *replied with a thoughtful answer.* **2.** Considerate: *a thoughtful gift.* [see *think*]

throne | thrōn | n. The chair on which a king, queen, or other person of high rank sits for ceremonies: *a throne of gold.* **thrones**

through | thrōō | prep. In one side and out the other: *through the house.* adj. Finished: *is through with the work.*

throw | thrō | v. To toss or send through the air: *will throw the basketball.* —**Throw out**—To get rid of. **throws, threw, throwing, thrown, thrower**

thrown | thrōn | v. Tossed: *had thrown his hat.* [see *throw*]

Thursday | thûrz′ dā′ | n. The fifth day of the week: *will meet on Thursday.* **Thurs.**

tickle | tĭk′əl | v. To touch lightly: *to tickle her toes.* **tickles, tickled, tickling, ticklish, tickler, ticklishness**

tickled | tĭk′əld | v. Touched lightly: *tickled until he laughed.* [see *tickle*]

tile | tīl | n. A thin piece of plastic, concrete, etc., used to cover floors or roofs: *removed the tile.* **tiles, tiled, tiling**

timid | tĭm′ĭd | adj. Shy: *a timid look.* **timidly, timidity, timidness**

total | tōt′l | adj. Complete or utter: *total confusion.* n. The full amount or sum: *a total of ten dollars.* **totals, totaled, totaling, totally, totality, totalization**

tour | tŏŏr | n. A trip in which several places of interest are seen: *an African tour.* **tours, toured, touring, tourist, tourism**

tournament | tŏŏr′nə mənt | n. A series of contests involving one sport: *a tennis tournament.* **tournaments, tourney**

towel | tou′əl | adj. For or related to a towel: *a towel bar.* n. A cloth or piece of paper used to dry things that are wet: *a fresh towel.* **towels, toweled, toweling**

traffic | trăf′ĭk | n. Cars, people, ships, etc., that are traveling at a particular time: *traffic on the highway.*

transport | trăns pôrt′ | v. To carry from one place to another: *to transport oil.* **transports, transported, transporting, transporter, transportation, transportable**

transportation | trăns′pər tā′shən | n. The means, such as a bus, train, etc., of going from one place to another: *depends on reliable transportation.* [see *transport*]

travel | trăv′əl | v. To go from one place to another: *will travel on a business trip.* **travels, traveled, traveling, traveler, travelers**

traveler | trăv′ə lər | n. A person going from one place to another: *a lonely traveler.* [see *travel*]

treat | trēt | v. 1. To behave toward: *to treat unfairly.* 2. To try to help or cure with some remedy: *will treat the disease.* **treats, treated, treating, treatable, treatment, treatments**

treatment | trēt′mənt | n. 1. Behavior toward something: *kind treatment.* 2. Something done or used to create relief; a cure: *medical treatment.* [see *treat*]

treaty | trē′tē | n. A formal written agreement between nations or states that includes terms of trade, etc.: *a peace treaty.* **treaties**

trial | trī′əl | n. 1. A test of something to check its quality, strength, fitness, etc.: *tested as a trial.* 2. An effort: *a trial to finish.* **trials**

trim | trĭm | v. To neaten by removing parts not needed: *will trim the branches.* **trims, trimmed, trimming, trimmer, trimmest, trimness**

trimmed | trĭmd | v. Neatened by removing parts not needed: *trimmed her hair.* [see *trim*]

truth | trŏŏth | n. The actual state of affairs: *spoke only the truth.* **truths, truthful, truthfully, truthfulness**

truthful | trŏŏth′fəl | adj. Honest: *a truthful witness.* [see *truth*]

twilight | twī′līt′ | adj. Of or related to twilight: *the twilight hours.* n. The faint light in the sky before the sun rises and after it sets: *will leave at twilight.* **twilights**

twist | twĭst | v. To turn or wind: *to twist the rope.* **twists, twisted, twisting, twister**

typewrite | tīp′rīt′ | v. To write with a typewriter: *will typewrite a memo.* **typewrites, typewrote, typewritten, typewriting, typewriter, typewriters**

typewriter | tīp′rī′tər | n. A machine for writing, which makes letters look like print: *an office typewriter.* [see *typewrite*]

U

umpire | ŭm′pīr′ | n. The person who rules on the plays in a game: *signal from the umpire.* **umpires, umpired, umpiring**

uncertain | ŭn sûr′tn | adj. 1. Apt to change: *uncertain forecast.* 2. Unsure or doubtful: *uncertain about the facts.* [see *certain*]

ă **pat** / ā **pay** / â **care** / ä **father** / ĕ **pet** / ē **be** / ĭ **pit** / ī **pie** / î **fierce** / ŏ **pot** / ō **go** / ô **paw, for** / oi **oil** / ŏŏ **book** /
ōō **boot** / ou **out** / ŭ **cut** / û **fur** / *th* **the** / th **thin** / hw **which** / zh **vision** / ə **ago, item, pencil, atom, circus**
©1977 by Houghton Mifflin Company. Reprinted by permission from THE AMERICAN HERITAGE SCHOOL DICTIONARY.

uneasy | ŭn ē′ zē | *adj.* Nervous or restless: *uneasy behavior.* [see *easy*]

union | yo͞on′yən | *n.* A group of workers united together to protect their interests: *belongs to the union. adj.* Of or related to a union: *union wages.* **unions, unionize, unionizes, unionized, unionizing**

unjust | ŭn jŭst′ | *adj.* Not fair: *an unjust rule.* [see *just*]

unpack | ŭn păk′ | *v.* To remove items packed away: *will unpack the trunk.* [see *pack*]

unwise | ŭn wīz′ | *adj.* Foolish: *an unwise choice.* [see *wise*]

use | yo͞oz | *v.* To put into service: *will use the machine.* **uses, used, using, useful, usefully, usefulness, useless, uselessly, uselessness**

useless | yo͞os′lĭs | *adj.* Not able to be used: *a useless tool.* [see *use*]

V

vacant | vā′kənt | *adj.* Empty: *a vacant room.* **vacantly, vacate, vacates, vacated, vacating, vacantness, vacancy**

vain | vān | *adj.* Overly prideful about one's appearance or abilities: *a vain and proud mayor.* **−In vain−**Without success. **vainly, vainness, vanity, vanities**

valuable | văl′yo͞o ə bəl | *adj.* Worth a lot of money: *a valuable necklace.* [see *value*]

value | văl′yo͞o | *n.* The worth or price of something: *of tremendous value.* **values, valued, valuing, valuably, valueless, valuate, valuable, valuables, valuation**

vanish | văn′ĭsh | *v.* To disappear suddenly: *to vanish from view.* **vanishes, vanished, vanishing**

vanity | văn′ĭ tē | *n.* Too much pride; boasting: *showed much vanity.* **−Vanity plate−**A special license plate made up of letters or numbers particularly requested by an owner of a car, truck, etc. [see *vain*]

various | vâr′ē əs | *adj.* Different: *various conclusions.* [see *vary*]

vary | vâr′ē | *v.* To make different: *to vary the menu.* **varies, varied, varying, various, variously, variety**

vegetable | vĕj′tə bəl | *n.* A plant whose seeds, leaves, roots, and fruit are used for food: *a crisp vegetable.* **vegetables**

velvet | vĕl′vĭt | *adj.* Of velvet: *a velvet hat. n.* Soft, thick, cloth made of rayon, silk, nylon, etc.: *a dress of velvet.* **velvets, velvety**

vice | vīs | *n.* A bad habit: *gave up his one vice.* **vices, vicious, viciously, viciousness**

victory | vĭk′tə rē | *n.* Triumph in a contest: *an unexpected victory.* **victories, victorious, victoriously, victoriousness, victor**

volcano | vŏl kā′nō | *n.* A hill or mountain built from the ash and lava that have erupted from the earth's crust: *an active volcano.* **volcanoes, volcanic**

volume | vŏl′yo͞om | *n.* **1.** Amount: *a tremendous volume of paper.* **2.** Loudness: *will turn down the volume.* **3.** One book from a set of books: *the sixth volume.* **volumes**

voyage | voi′ĭj | *n.* A long journey: *a sea voyage.* **voyages, voyaged, voyaging, voyager**

vulgar | vŭl′gər | *adj.* Showing lack of taste or manners: *a vulgar laugh.* **vulgarly, vulgarity**

W

wander | wŏn′dər | *v.* To travel here and there without purpose: *wander for hours.* **wanders, wandered, wandering, wanderer**

warehouse | wâr′hous′ | *n.* A building where goods are stored: *kept at the warehouse.* **warehouses**

wealth | wĕlth | *n.* Riches or property: *inherited wealth.* **wealthy, wealthier, wealthiest, wealthily, wealthiness**

weave | wēv | *v.* To make a finished product by interlacing threads: *weave a blanket.* **weaves, weaved, weaving, wove, woven, weaver**

week | wēk | *n.* Seven days: *absent for a week.* **weeks, weekly**

weekly | wēk′lē | *adj.* Once each week: *a weekly meeting.* [see *week*]

weight | wāt | *n.* How heavy something is: *height and weight.* **weights, weighty, weigh, weighs, weighed, weighing, weightless, weightlessness, weigher**

whether | wĕ*th*′ər | *conj.* A word that expresses a choice or an alternative: *whether to go.*

whisper | wĭs′pər | *n.* A soft, low tone of voice: *to speak in a whisper.* **whispers, whispered, whispering**

whistle | wĭs′əl | *n.* A high-pitched sound: *a loud whistle.* **whistles, whistled, whistling, whistler**

width | wĭdth | *n.* The distance across something: *a width of ten feet.* **widths**

wise | wīz | *adj.* Showing good sense; smart: *a wise decision.* **unwise, unwisely**

wool | wŏŏl | *n.* The soft fur of sheep: *a coat made of wool.* **wools, wooly, woolier, wooliest, woolen, woolens**

woolen | wŏŏl′ən | *adj.* Made from wool: *woolen socks.* [see *wool*]

wrap | răp | *v.* **1.** To cover something by folding and tying paper around it: *will wrap the book.* **2.** To wind around: *will wrap the string around it.* **wraps, wrapped, wrapping, wrapper**

wrapped | răpt | *v.* **1.** Covered with paper and tied: *wrapped the package.* **2.** To draw or wind around: *wrapped it around her.* [see *wrap*]

wrench | rĕnch | *n.* A tool for turning bolts and nuts: *used a heavy wrench.* **wrenches, wrenched, wrenching**

COVER DESIGN:
Design Five

PHOTOGRAPHY:
Joseph Sachs
Stock Photo's Inc.

TEXT ILLUSTRATIONS:
John Edwards & Associates
    pages 14, 21, 87, 111, 133

Tracy Sabin
    pages 7, 31, 67, 95, 139

All other art by Will Winslow

PROJECT ASSISTANCE:
Book Production Systems, Inc.

ă **pat** / ā **pay** / â **care** / ä **father** / ĕ **pet** / ē **be** / ĭ **pit** / ī **pie** / î **fierce** / ŏ **pot** / ō **go** / ô **paw, for** / oi **oil** / ŏŏ **book** / ōō **boot** / ou **out** / ŭ **cut** / û **fur** / *th* **the** / th **thin** / hw **which** / zh **vision** / ə **ago, item, pencil, atom, circus**